Howard J. Ruff

Famine and Survival in America

LITHOGRAPHED IN U S A BY
PUBLISHERS PRESS
SALT LAKE CITY UTAH

Library of Congress Catalog Card Number: 74-20686
First Edition 1974
First Printing October 1974
Second Printing December 1974
Third Printing January 1975

Typography by Column Type Co., Inc.

Contents

Why This Book Was Written

Late in 1973, I found myself at a bookstand in the airport at Miami, Florida, looking for something to read on a flight home. A title caught my eye, "*How to Prepare for the Coming Crash*" by Robert Preston. That didn't sound like a good book to read on an airplane, but I bought it anyway.

The flight to San Francisco was spent engrossed, first, in the book; second, in my personal plans for my family.

Mr. Preston convinced me (and scared me in the process) that governmental inflationary and monetary policies were leading us inevitably toward a gigantic depression worse than the 1930's. I realized that if this were true, it was necessary to prepare my family for survival, by storing the necessities and making appropriate investments.

Mr. Preston's book was only the beginning. Further research revealed several other even more pressing reasons why our food supply is so threatened that a point of no return may have been passed.

The conclusions I reached are what this book is all about.

Three major influences have led to the solutions I am proposing.

First, I love children. I have 8 of my own, plus a foster-son. The thought of children suffering from lack of preparedness both frightens and horrifies me.

Second, my religious heritage has prepared me emotionally for the concept of an emergency food supply. For more than 40 years, my church leaders have been recommending that we store a minimum of one year's supply of food and clothing, as well as other necessities. I had not done it, and I seem to be in a lot of good company. According to figures gathered from one of the food storage companies, less than 6% of the members of my Church have an adequate emergency program, despite the Church leaders' warnings. Even though I was not completely prepared before this, I at least *knew* I should be.

Third, I have spent years in intensive study of nutrition. This was not my specialty in college, but that may be an advantage. I have no biases in this fascinating field. Fortunately, I have some very special study skills acquired during 8 years as owner of a speed reading school. This has enabled me to survey virtually all the literature in the fields that relate to my subject matter, and stay current on all new data.

This comprehensive survey revealed a shocker!

Those who are storing food are making serious nutritional errors in their programs.

Even those who think they are properly prepared may watch their families' health deteriorate, and as they weaken, many will be carried away prematurely in the epidemics that always accompany famines — this on what they erroneously assume is an adequate diet.

The purpose of this book is five-fold:

1. To help to awaken you, or perhaps even frighten

you into facing some facts regarding the food crisis which is rushing upon us, and in fact is already here.

2. To prepare a survival manual for my immediate family and relatives.

3. To set straight the myths and misconceptions — I call them "the Deadly Errors" — about emergency food storage, that I have been hearing for years. These myths are based on lack of knowledge of the latest research in bio-chemistry and nutrition. If these myths are not countered, people will have deceptively full stomachs and, at the same time, suffer from malnutrition.

4. To help you judge the merits of the commercial storage programs — a "consumer's guide," if you please.

5. To offer a practical plan of attack on the problem. The first part of this book may frighten you because the facts are truly frightening. I fully expect this to anger some people. In ancient times it was often the custom for the King to kill the messenger who brought the bad news. But the last section should remove all fear, as there is a way to prepare, and receive the calm assurance that will come from being ready.

Before you get too far underway, we might as well face one problem squarely. I am so concerned about the problems described in the book that I am now involved in the marketing and sale of commodities like some of those I'm recommending, and I have not spared criticism of those commodities, if I felt they have disadvantages that you should know about. You will have to judge for yourself my objectivity and the merits of my ideas and act accordingly. Had it not been for my professional experience in the marketing, sale, *and proper use* of nutritional concentrates, coupled with my thorough survey of the scientific literature, this book would have never been written. I simply would not have had the knowledge, the background, nor the interest.

I would like to offer my thanks to two people.

Harry Browne, author of *"You Can Profit From a Monetary Crisis"* influenced my thinking on inflation, and I have leaned heavily on him in Chapter II.

And second, a great lady, Adelle Davis, through her marvelous controversial books, introduced me to the wonderful world of nutrition and natural foods. She passed away just two days before I began writing this book, but for me, she will never die.

How to Read This Book

If you already believe in food storage, but have done nothing about it, or if you believe in food storage and have started a storage program, *no matter how complete you think it is,* start at Part II, "The Deadly Errors," then go to Part III, then back to Part I. If you are new to the whole concept of storage, or unconvinced as to the need for storage, or if you think you can safely procrastinate, then run, don't walk, to Part I and start at the beginning. Powerful forces are already in motion, and the time is short. It may be too late now, as many of the things we discuss here can literally happen overnight!

I hope and pray I'm wrong about the problems ahead, as I love the world in which I live. I want my children to go to college, go on a 2 year mission for my church, and raise kids in a comfortable world. I want them to bring my grandchildren for visits on Father's Day and Christmas.

Let's hope the troubles are brief, one or two years at the most, and life will be beautiful again. But above all, let's survive. If you believe I'm full of prunes, and do nothing, remember – *you are gambling with your life and your children's lives.* If I'm right and you act promptly, you have nothing to lose, and you gain peace of mind, and incidentally, make a fine investment in the process.

Finally, it is only right to state that some of the concepts in this book are controversial, and I have taken sides on some issues where the experts are not agreed. This especially relates to the nutrition sections. It could very well be that some of the experts will take exception to what I have said. That's good. If it stimulates debate, and that debate is carried on a high plane, knowledge will be advanced.

The opinions expressed are my own and if there are errors, no one is responsible for them. I believe the research on which I base my conclusions is accurate, true and sound. As I broaden my knowledge, and as new research is unveiled, I will modify those opinions if necessary in subsequent editions. Life and growth is change. I don't mind finding out if I'm wrong on something. I hate, however, to *be* wrong, because I live every principle I espouse. My studies have not stopped with publication of this book.

Part I
The Vulnerable Necessity

Our food supply is in deadly danger. That's hard to believe, even for me, knowing what I know. As I write these words, I just returned from having dinner at a wonderful restaurant. We had a magnificent meal, and all we wanted. The only jarring note was the bill, which was 40% higher than the last time I ate there a few months ago. But behind this apparent plenty is a rapidly disintegrating foundation.

A deadly combination of conditions are coming together sometime soon to rob us of our food. And that's what Part I is all about.

CHAPTER I

Years of Plenty, Years of Famine

Have you ever met a reformed drunk? For years he drank and convinced himself there was nothing wrong with drinking. Then something happened and he saw the light. From that time on he has to tell the world.

That's how I feel about emergency food storage. I had heard for years of the necessity for an emergency supply of food. In fact, since the 1930s, Church leaders have urged us to store food.

It was not without precedent. Every child in Sunday School has heard the story of Joseph in Egypt who prophesied of seven years of plenty followed by seven years of famine. Pharaoh was so impressed he made Joseph second in command in Egypt. Sure enough, they had seven great years, and were able to store enough to get them through the seven bad years.

I think the remarkable thing about this story is that Pharaoh had the good sense to follow this advice. And how fortunate that he had seven years to prepare! We could have used a Pharaoh 5 or 6 years ago.

It wasn't until a few months ago that I realized I had had twenty years of adult life to prepare, and I had done nothing.

My wife, Kay, had seen that we had stored some wheat and canned goods a few years back, and they had come in real handy when we had a severe business failure in 1968. She had laboriously acquired a few things without much money, and with no help from me. I just couldn't get excited about the urgency of storing food when all my life the supermarkets had been full of food whenever I wanted to buy some. In fact, this nation had been plagued with farm surpluses which had been bought by the Government for tens of billions of dollars, in order to support prices for the benefit of farmers, so we could pay more money for our food. (That last sentence doesn't make sense, but that's the Government's fault, not mine, so I'll leave it the way it is.)

As I explained in the foreword, when I bought Robert Preston's book in the Miami Airport, *"How to Prepare for the Coming Crash"*, and read it through twice on the flight home, it had a tremendous impact on me, and started a chain of events that is still adding new links each day.

First, I looked at the commercial and do-it-yourself food storage programs, and found them dangerously wanting. My years as a nutrition counselor and writer had prepared me to develop my own program for my own family, once I decided to do it. When I saw the deadly errors my friends were making with their own storage programs, I knew I had to do something for them, and this book is the result. If it is read and applied, it will save lives.

Second, I began to research the factors that could lead to a food crisis. I discovered the fact that should be obvious to everyone, but apparently isn't. I found that of the three basic physical necessities — food, shelter, and clothing, *food is by far the most vulnerable.* And most shocking of all, never has our food supply been so endangered in this country as it is today!

Let's look at the factors that could interrupt the flow of food we have taken for granted all our lives.

Transportation

If the trucks and trains were to stop rolling, the supermarkets would be empty in a matter of hours, and they could be the scene of rioting by desperate people.

Labor Problems

There are several segments of organized labor, goaded by inflation and inter-union jurisdictional disputes, that could stop the growing, harvesting, processing, and distribution of foods in a day.

The Weather

If we had one bad weather year, sufficient to cut production by 20%, hunger would stalk the land, as we have zero reserves.

Overseas Demand

As world population grows, and drought in Asia and Africa creates famine, pressures develop to send more of our food overseas. This is how we lost our reserves.

Inflation and Depression

This subject will get a lot of attention here, as I believe our economy is in terrible trouble, and we can become so economically crippled that food production will become disrupted and distribution impossible.

All of these factors are not only possible, but probable. Let's tackle them one at a time. I will show you how these problems are not just the same old problems that were only minor irritants to most of us before now. They have become ticking time bombs, and some are already starting to explode.

CHAPTER II

The Bursting Balloon

Unfortunately, when presented with a current or potential calamity, we often tend to respond with conditioned reflexes, denying the facts, if they're unpleasant enough, or if they come from an unexpected source.

One of my favorite cartoons shows a Red Cross worker in a boat, knocking on a door of a house with water over the front porch, and a rapidly rising flood. A sleepy voice from the second floor bedroom says, "Who is it?" The worker replies, "The Red Cross", to which the voice responds, "I gave at the office".

To even state the possibility of the collapse of the American economy, or monetary system, sounds paranoid on the face of it. It smacks of small groups of doomsayers meeting in secret hideouts with the blinds pulled down, or old men in robes and beards with sandwich boards announcing the end of the world.

Unfortunately, the possibility of collapse has become so real, that some of our most respected orthodox economists are beginning to seriously consider the possibility.

I have read speeches by Arthur Burns, Chairman of the Federal Reserve Board, and David Rockefeller of Chase Manhattan Bank, raising the spectre of economic panic.

I also hear reassuring statements from bankers, brokers and bureaucrats pooh-poohing the "prophets of doom and gloom".

Where is the truth? I believe we will see very soon, possibly before you read this. In this section I am concerned about 5 things: runaway inflation, depression, bank failures, currency collapse, governmental collapse, and their effect on our food supply.

Runaway Inflation

The story is told of the modern Rip Van Winkle, who goes to sleep in 1974 and wakes up in 1984. His first thought is to find a pay phone and call his broker. He checks on his IBM stock which was worth $25,000 when he went to sleep, and finds to his delight and amazement it is now worth $3,000,000. Just then the operator breaks in and says, "Your 3 minutes are up. Please deposit $7,000!"

Harry Browne, an investment counselor and author, has written a book which is must reading, "*You Can Profit From a Monetary Crisis*". He details the steps by which an "acceptable" rate of inflation turns into a runaway inflation.

"Inflation affects the government, just as it affects consumers. For the government is the largest single purchaser of products and services in the nation. As inflation pushes the general price levels higher and higher, the government has to pay more for what it buys than it had budgeted.

"One of the reasons why federal deficits usually turn out to be bigger than predicted is that the government has budgeted on the basis of prices at the beginning of the fiscal year. By the time the year ends, prices are a good deal higher — causing the government to go further into the red to cover the costs.

"And, of course, the added deficit is financed by inflation. So the government is much like a cat chasing its tail. It inflates, suffers high prices because of the inflation, and so must inflate further, but then suffers even higher prices, requiring even more inflation, etc. For a long time, the effect upon the government may be small. But the compounding of inflation must reach substantial proportions eventually".

For example, *U.S. News and World Report* for June 17, 1974, examined the difference between estimated cost, and actual costs in Pentagon weapons purchasing as reported by the General Accounting Office. 55 major weapons systems are 26.3 billions above estimates and rising — over 7 billions in the last 6 months of 1973 alone! The first reason given is inflation. It caused 2.5 billions of the 7 billion 1973 increases!

The basic problem is an expansion of the money supply, due to continued Federal deficits.

When the Government spends more than it takes in, it's no different from you and me. It has to pay its bills. If it raises taxes to cover its deficit, it usually soaks "big business", because it doesn't want to get "the people" mad. Businesses then raise prices to cover their tax costs. This makes "the people" mad, but at "big business", not the government.

The easiest way politically for the government to operate, is to borrow money from the Federal Reserve. It just signs "notes" (bonds, certificates, etc.) which it sells to the Federal Reserve, and the Federal Reserve creates (out of nothing) a bank deposit for the government to draw on, and the Government writes checks on it, just as though it were real money. *This dilutes the value of every dollar in circulation.* It's as though you were at an auction, and everyone present was given 10% more money. You can bet that prices would be bid up at least 10% higher.

The basic problem is an expansion of the money supply, due to continued Federal deficits.

The theory is that this new "money" is backed by increases in the amount of goods and services produced in America. Even if this were true, which it is not, at the time of this writing our present rate of inflation of our currency, according to government figures, is 12.5%, and the amount of goods and services has *declined* for two straight quarters.

Inflation is *not* an increase in prices, although prices do increase. *It is a decrease in the value of your money.* It means every dollar buys less. I don't trust Government statistics. We have already seen for weeks and months the spectacle of high Government officials lying and getting caught at it. If it serves their purpose, they will distort the figures *toward the optimistic.*

It has been said that a government statistic is like a bikini. What it reveals is interesting, but what it conceals is vital.

Let's see what the Government tries as a cure for inflation, and what the chance is for success.

1. Cut spending.

No way! No matter what the politicians say, it won't happen until too late. Too many people yelling things like "If we can put men on the moon, why can't we:

(Choose one)

☐ Stop unemployment by creating government jobs!
☐ Feed all the poor!
☐ Clean up all the rivers and the air!
☐ Provide a guaranteed income for everyone!
☐ Your pet project!

All these things are desirable, beyond question, but they all involve spending money we don't have! There are powerful political forces behind each proposal, and our elected officials feel strongly about employment and jobs — their own. "He who robs Peter to pay Paul, will always have the vote of Paul".

The "Fed"

The Federal Reserve has a vested interest in continued Government budget deficits. Why?

Because it is a privately owned banking system whose principal income is derived from loaning the government money to finance its deficits!

In 1971, the Government sent over $18 billion into the pockets of the bankers who own the Federal Reserve banking system, as interest payments on Government securities owned by the banks — the interest on the national debt!

And the Federal Reserve is not subject to audit or any kind of accounting! Attempts by Congress to pass such laws have been beaten back. It is contrary to the self-interest of the Fed for the government to reduce spending!

2. Increase taxes.

In classic economic theory, this is supposed to pull money out of circulation, reduce spending, and the competitive market drives prices down. *But its actual net effect is to force merchants to increase prices so they can have a net profit after their increased taxes.* It backfires by increasing the demands of labor for wage and benefit increases to cover their taxes — which forces up prices. So your dollar buys less. You can't put out a fire by pouring kerosene on it.

3. Tighten the money supply and increase interest rates!

Have you noticed that the Fed's first choice of inflation fighting tools is to increase their own income with higher interest rates?

As I write this, the prime lending rate is 11½% and there is a real credit crunch. This means that everyone who needs some kind of financing or equity capital has trouble getting it—*except the government.* As interest rates for business go up, it is simply passed on to you, the consumer. Higher mortgage rates prevailing in July of 1974 (10%) mean that you would pay $23,000 more in interest over the life of a 30 year mortgage on a $35,000 house, than you would have before interest rates started up in November 1973 (7%), just 9 months earlier. Also, the builder has higher construction loan costs, which, of course, he adds to the price of the house. This is fighting inflation?

4. Wage and Price Controls?

They don't work. This only builds up explosive pressures for upward movement, creates shortages, and forces the producers into bankruptcy, which reduces the supply, and forces price increases and/or shortages — with a high priced black market.

The Only Solution

The only solution that will really reduce inflation is to reduce government spending, and retire the national debt. This, however, means millions of government workers out of jobs, government subsidies eliminated, government contracts cancelled, and the worst depression in our history. No politician wants to be blamed for this. (The Democrats have been running against Hoover since 1930.)

A worse depression will come anyway, through Runaway Inflation, as we pass the point of no return, where stopping it is so painful that no one has the guts to take the necessary action.

There are our only two choices: a horrible depression, or a devastating runaway inflation. In either instance, the growing, processing and distribution of food could become next to impossible.

If inflation doesn't scare you, let's let Harry Browne describe a Runaway Inflation in his book *"You Can Profit From a Monetary Crisis"*.

> "I believe we can create a scenario to show the development of inflation over the length of its cycle. The scenario encompasses the histories of many past inflations, along with some speculation concerning what might happen if inflation is continued to its ultimate conclusion in the United States.
>
> 1. Over a period of years, retail prices go up only gradually — if the government hasn't been too ambitious in its programs. During that time, price increases are small enough that they're noticeable on an annual basis only.
>
> 2. However, the inevitable compounding of inflation leads to a point where consumers become concerned about constantly rising prices. In addition, the gold supply may be jeopardized by foreign claims.
>
> 3. If the government respects these market reactions, it will show some frugality, cut its

spending, and diminish the inflation. This will result in a recession. If the government fails to heed the market signals and tries to avoid the recession, inflation will continue in earnest.

4. If the cycle is allowed to continue, there will be a period, perhaps of several years, during which inflation will be a national concern. Prices will be rising steadily and substantially; there will be concern about the losses suffered by people on fixed incomes. But nothing will be done to halt the inflation.

5. Eventually inflation will be noticeable on a monthly basis, instead of just annually. A consumer may notice that an item he buys regularly has gone up in price several times during a few months. If that happens with a number of things he buys, inflation has reached an advanced stage.

6. If the government heeds this belated warning, it will finally capitulate to the General Market and stop the inflation. This, of course, will initiate a full-scale depression.

Acceleration of the Cycle

7. If the government is unwilling to allow that to happen, it will continue the inflation despite the warnings from the market. Then the flight from paper money takes place in earnest. Many individuals will rush to get rid of their dollars before they depreciate further — exchanging them for gold, silver, gold-

backed foreign currencies, or commodities usable to the buyer in the future.

8. The original compounding effect at the government level now reaches crisis proportions. Government employees won't settle for the same old wages, even with a nominal "cost-of-living" increase built in. And inflation has reached the point where prices of the supplies the government needs have reached extraordinary levels. So the government must pay higher wages and prices — immediately. It can do this only by inflating the currency at a faster rate.

9. Naturally, the new inflation makes everything even worse. Prices rush upward. Weekly price changes become the rule at the retail level. Soon, products formerly costing a few dollars are priced in the hundreds of dollars.

10. The government is caught on a merry-go-round it can't stop. Tax-collectors, policemen, and bureaucrats who once received $15,000 per year, for example, are now paid $500 per day. But even that isn't enough for them to keep up with skyrocketing prices. Most of them could do something else for $1,000 per day — even without special skills. To keep them, and to purchase supplies, the government must offer market prices and wages. If it doesn't, the government itself will

collapse — for lack of tax-collectors and policemen.

11. Soon, prices increase every day. And the prices of the simplest items are measured in thousands and millions of dollars. Again, the government must step up its inflation in order to hold onto its employees.

12. Eventually, prices change by the hour. Workers demand to be paid twice-daily or more often, in order to rush out to spend the paper money before it depreciates further. The government, still caught in a dilemma of its own making, must print the money even faster — or go under. Million-dollar bills come off the presses in the quantities that one-dollar bills were printed a year earlier. And the bills may be printed on only one side — to save time and ink.

13. Even though the government wouldn't stop the inflation earlier because it wanted to avoid a depression, there is depression — along with runaway inflation. For "business as usual" can't be carried on during a runaway inflation. It's too difficult to trade and produce. Factories close from inability to keep up with the inflation.

14. By this time, the government is clearly licked. It must halt the printing press orgy and return to sanity. There's only one way this can be done. It has to introduce a new

currency that's backed by gold or silver and can be converted into gold or silver by anyone. Nothing less would give the new money any stability. And, of course, the old currency would be totally worthless. This isn't a new problem to savers; they will have lost the value of their savings long before.

If the government introduces a new gold-backed currency, the economy can begin the long road back to normality. There will be gigantic losses to be liquidated, plants to be reopened, jobs to be found. And all that must be done with less efficient communications and mobility than would have been available had the government surrendered to the market earlier.

The Ultimate Disaster

15. But what if the government has no gold or silver with which to back a new currency? What if it has long since squandered all of its real wealth? And what if there's no foreign government or others who will lend it the gold necessary? Clearly, saving the dollar will no longer be in the interest of any foreign government at that point.

In that case, the monetary system will collapse entirely. There will be no way that individuals can use billions of dollars, depreciating hourly, to trade and exchange for necessities.

The currency will be totally worthless because no one will be willing to accept it.

The currency will fail and, with it, the government. For the government will have no resources with which to pay for what it needs to survive.

Throughout the marketplace, normal exchange will come to a halt. Chaos will reign as all the normal trappings of civilization as we know it disappear. There will be no law, no order, no communications other than verbal, no companies to turn to for help.

16. Exchanges can occur then only on a barter basis, such as trading a loaf of bread for a gallon of gas. But precious little bartering can take place. For it's practically impossible for a large company to employ thousands of workers on a barter basis. So who will produce the loaf of bread or the gallon of gas? After current supplies have been exhausted, only what's been hoarded in advance can be bartered.

Individuals in rural areas will have a very difficult time living at subsistence levels. They'll need to have marketable commodities stored with which to barter for surplus food with those who are growing it. Individuals living in cities may not survive at all.

17. When the worst of the aftermath of runaway inflation has passed, barter may

evolve to the point where exchanges become more frequent and more extended, covering longer distances and bigger trades.

Commodities in especially high demand (such as food, cigarettes, liquor) may be used as money. An individual would accept them in exchange even if he doesn't intend to use them himself. He'll know that he can always trade them to someone else for some thing he wants. They will have accepted value and be widely needed. This, of course, is the same way that money came into existence originally.

18. Eventually, however, a more useful trading medium will probably assert itself — most likely coins of real silver or gold. As the coins feed through the community, a semblance of order will return. A durable money commodity is the lifeblood of civilization — making possible the specialization of labor, the ability of one person to employ another, the opportunity to accumulate long-term savings.

And so, from the ashes of a dead civilization, a new one arises — painfully, slowly, and probably fully prepared to make the same mistakes that eventually killed the old one.

Once step 5 has been reached, the economy is in for rough going — no matter which choices the government makes

thereafter.[1] But if step 15 is reached, in which
no valuable currency can replace the old one,
the doom of the country is sealed".

Survival First

With such a scenario, survival becomes your first responsibility, and the protection of your family is your first concern. You need a safe place, adequate storable foods for one to five years, and a supply of all the commodities necessary for orderly life. You will also need a medium of exchange. I have chosen *food* as my medium of exchange. After meeting my family's nutritional needs, I will store in a safe place as much storable food as I can buy, and when our currency is worthless, I will be able to barter it for anything I need.

I'm also following Browne's investment suggestions in foreign currency, gold, and silver, but my emphasis is on food.

How About Timing

When will it be too late to do anything about it and put in a supply of food?

1. When food prices rise to a point where you can't afford to buy enough for safety. (This is an individual matter. You may have already passed the point where

[1] I believe that's where we were in late 1973.

you can buy enough. Buy what you can!)

2. When any event, such as those discussed in later chapters, touches off a food buying panic. (Truck strike, government emergency measures, gas shortages, bank runs, etc.)

3. Shortly after a major food crop falls seriously below expectations. (That's happened once already!)

4. When 5% of the population, or less, gets nervous and decides to store a year's supply of food.

Here's the frightening arithmetic. Our food reserves are down to 23 days for the whole population. If 100% of the people decided to store a 2 day supply of food, it would wipe out all available supplies! If 50% of the people decided on 46 days storage, the effect would be the same! Let's chart it out:

100% could store a 23 day supply
50% could store a 46 day supply
25% could store a 92 day supply
10% could store a 230 day supply
6.3% could store a one year supply

But long before that 6.3% had completed their purchasing, the panic and increased prices caused by that much buying would have made it impossible. When reserves are obviously getting too low, the government will move in to buy up food to "prevent panic" and assure its food requirements for the Armed Forces and welfare recipients. **I feel that between 1% and 3% of our population will be able to systematically and quietly store food**

before it's too late, and it's strictly first come, first served.

Could this book cause such a panic? I doubt it. I fully expect it to sell no more than 100,000 copies, and only a small percentage of those who read it will do anything about it.

I've had friends say, "I couldn't stand to be well fed while others are starving". Only well fed people make statements like that. People who say that haven't thought it through. When *your* family is starving, you don't care about anyone but them — their very life. I yield to no one in concern for the general welfare, but my concern for my children and wife comes first. I will do anything necessary to ensure their survival, including defending them if necessary.

ACCELERATING THE PACE

The Humpty-Dumpty Syndrome

All my life I've been told that banks could not fail today, like they did in the 1930's. Perhaps some Government economist will explain it to me again, because it doesn't look too good to me now.

Banks are terribly vulnerable and their collapse could by-pass several steps of our destructive process. Here's how it can happen:

As inflation rates increase, the amount of interest bank pay depositors is too low to stay even. This is also true of Savings and Loans, Thrift Companies, Credit

Unions, and Insurance cash values! It even outstrips the return on mortgages. The depositor, with good reason, loses confidence and looks for a better return for his money. He figures thusly:

	$1,000	in the bank
	6.5%	Interest
	$ 65	Return
Less	− 13	Income tax (I figured at a low 20%)
	$ 52	Net before inflation
	−125	Inflation tax (loss of purchasing power at 12.5%)
	$ [73]	Net Loss (7.3%)

That ain't no way to get rich!

This process of withdrawal from savings institutions to look for higher returns is call "disintermediation". The investor looks for alternative investments, because he probably is counting on some return on his savings for income to help meet inflation.

The stock market looks too dangerous. Public concern about high interest rates, and general uncertainty, make the market's performance dubious at best.

Sidney Allen, the respected Financial Editor of the San Francisco Chronicle, said in his column "*The Money Game*" on July 20, 1974:

> "It isn't only the rarified level of short-term interest rates that continues to bug this stock market.

"It's also the great credibility gap over corporate profit. Company after company has reported gains, some startlingly large over last year. But there's little or no market reaction.

"Let a company slip just slightly, though, or even show a good gain but one slightly below expectations, and its shares hit the skids. You've seen it happen again and again.

"Credibility is the cause, the culprit.

"It is not that we doubt the figures as released. It is, however, that there's a deep rooted suspicion about the quality of those profits.

"A dollar isn't necessarily a dollar, nowadays. So more and more profits are being suspected, like our sandwich coins, of being padded with filler. Their primary filler, of course, consists on inventory gains.

"This is one of the funny money blooms of inflation that looks beautiful, for a moment. But of course it wilts away with the purchase of the very next batch of inventory.

"It's probably inevitable, then, that we'd come to regard it as something not quite real, as a ghost that passes in the night. Nobody knows quite how to figure it, so nobody really believes it.

"Another price of double-digit inflation, then, is that profit looks good but the marketplace still feels bad. A reminder that the quality of profits, like the quality of living in such a hyped-up period, is at least a bit incredible.

"And potentially gangrenous to the capital life-blood of our economy.

"When contemplating what is real and what is illusory, it is well to keep in mind that inflation is truly another tax.

"And taxes are also inflationary to costs.

"For instance, Harry M. Hansen of Marin County reminds that in order for a corporation to retain one dollar of profit it must earn two. The corporate income tax rate is 50 per cent.

"What it adds up to, says Hansen, is this: a corporation needs to earn 22 per cent book profit this year just to break even. For the tax collector takes half, leaving 11 per cent. And this year's annual rate of inflation of 11 per cent would eat up the remainder.

"Consequently, if the corporation hopes to pay a fair dividend to its stockholders it would have to earn a book profit substantially greater. Priming the inflation pump in the process, probably.

"The exercise surely serves to indicate that inflation, on top of federal and state income taxes, is a capital confiscator so ravenous as to be ruinous".

Real estate is less and less attractive as interest rates and costs are pricing homes out of the market. In my home town of Danville, California, prices of homes went up 10% in the first six months of 1974, but hardly anyone is buying them. They are sitting unsold!

The only things increasing in value fast enough to keep up with inflation are basic commodities: Gold, silver, metals, paper, food, lumber, certain chemicals and gold-backed foreign currencies.

The first major sign of possible bank collapse is an accelerating flow of funds from savings institutions into these commodities. The banks cannot lose deposits indefinitely without failing. *As of this writing, the outflow has begun and is accelerating.* This has forced the banks to borrow money at high rates from individuals on 90-day Certificates of Deposit (C.D.'s) while lending for longer periods. That's fine as long as investors renew their C.D.'s every 90 days. But what if investors begin to worry and refuse to renew? Then banks start calling loans.

Let's see what Sidney Allen had to say about that:

> "Every money man knows the hazards of borrowing short and lending long. If anything goes awry, it can be very embarrassing, even financially devastating.
>
> "That's not exactly where the banks are just at present. Still, they are playing a variation of the hazardous game.
>
> "They are borrowing short, via 90-day Certificates of Deposit. (C.D.'s) to get the money to meet their heavy loan demands. The reason they are doing this, of course, is "disintermediation".

> "That is, funds they might ordinarily be getting on deposit are going somewhere else, diverted by the lure of better interest returns. So banks in need have to compete as best they can, via the C.D.'s.
>
> "In their scramble for funds with which to expand, overseas as well as at home in this multinational world, banks have put out more than $70 billion of C.D.'s. As these come due the banks have to re-borrow the money by renewing the C.D.'s.
>
> "Or else, horror of horrors, by dumping investments and calling loans to pay them off. Dumping investments could expose some badly emaciated bank corpuses, what with today's so high interest rates.
>
> "And calling loans could pull down the house that Jack built.
>
> "Anything that shakes the faith in banks, then, can be anathema. So it's no wonder that prayers have been said, and fingers crossed, since the Franklin Bank scandal and scare."

The banks are terrified over the possibility of failure of a major bank. It could produce incredible disintermediation, toppling banks like dominoes. This is why when Franklin Bank omitted their dividend, due, they claimed, to $27 million in losses (which finally turned out to be over $67 million) due to bad foreign exchange transactions, the Federal Reserve loaned them *$1 billion 450 million* by June 1974 to keep them afloat. Franklin Bank lost so many deposits and C.D.'s to nervous withdrawals, they will need over $2 billion before the outflow stops. *This is the 20th largest bank in America! How many such loans can the Federal Reserve make?* What is the real story? By the time you read this, you may know the answers to these questions. And it won't be pretty.

If banks start failing, due to runs caused by disintermediation, the Federal Deposit Insurance Corp. has only enough funds to protect about 2% of the bank deposits in America!

That's fine as long as only occasionally a small bank fails. But what if we have three or four Franklin Banks?

The banks have only enough currency on hand to meet an immediate demand for less than 7% of the funds on deposit, the lowest since 1929! They can be forced to call loans, triggering panic, business collapses and depression, or they can dump their investments, forcing a collapse of the real estate, stock and bond markets, destroying their own profits and income from these investments.

As further indication of the nervousness in the more sophisticated segments of our financial community, the recent prospectus of a conservative Bond and Money Market mutual fund, the Capital Preservation Fund, makes an interesting statement regarding redemption of shares by investors.

". . . Should payment by check be impossible at any time, such payment will be made by postal money order". *(San Francisco Chronicle,* June 14, 1974, p. 61.)

How's that for an expression of confidence in our banking system?

The Effect on Food

If the banks collapse, depression hits us, or runaway inflation becomes the order of the day, food will disappear. Processors, distributors and transporters will collapse also. Chaos, riots, and destruction will stalk the land until some kind of new order arises. When it happens, will you want to be on the streets competing with the mob for food? Or would you rather be sitting in your own home, or a safe retreat, knowing you wouldn't have to come out for a year or more, that you had all the essentials for secure survival in optimum health for you and your children until order is restored?

CHAPTER III

The Achilles Heel — Labor, Distribution, and Civil Paranoia

In a March 1974 column, Jack Anderson, the syndicated columnist said,

> "... The oil shortage could be compounded this year by a food shortage, because food stocks have dropped to the lowest level in 20 years.
>
> All it would take would be minor crop failures or transportation tie-ups to cause basic foods to start disappearing from the supermarket shelves.
>
> Agriculture Department sources have told us the nation would be in "awful shape" for food if the delicate food delivery system should be fouled up.
>
> ... The meat outlook isn't much better. 'A two-week tie-up in the transportation system could cause serious meat shortages', an Agriculture Department expert told us. 'The

> meat delivery system has only about a four-to five day flexibility; after that, the shelves would start looking bare'.
>
> . . . Transportation foul-ups are not uncommon. A few weeks ago, chain stores had to rely on their own reserves for a few days because of transportation problems. A more troublesome tie-up could cause serious shortages".

If the nation's food distribution system should break down, it would take from 2 to 7 days for our supermarket shelves to become empty — if there was no panic. Panic, under such circumstances, however, is a sure thing. **If you wait to store food until it's apparent to everyone there's going to be a shortage, then it's too late. You can't get insurance when the barn is on fire!** Your only choices could be to starve, or to join the mob and try to grab an armful. I can visualize supermarkets gutted and burned, and people trampled. Panic is a strange and powerful force.

Famines creep up on us slowly enough that we can see them coming and prepare. But transportation, labor and distribution problems can happen so fast there is no time to prepare.

Strikes — Expected and Unexpected

I once owned a thriving franchise in the speed-reading school business in Northern California. In January of 1968 I had decided to put all my advertising eggs in one basket, by printing an 8-page supplement section to be distributed in the *Sunday San Francisco Chronicle,* the second weekend in January. These supplements cost me $25,000, and were geared toward a series of meetings to be held the following week. These January classes represented about half our business for the year.

On Friday afternoon, an illegal wildcat strike hit the *Los Angeles Examiner* and shut it down. The next morning, the *San Francisco Examiner* and *Chronicle* were struck with an illegal secondary boycott, in the form of a sympathy strike. There went $25,000 down the drain. The printed supplements were useless because they were aimed at public meetings at specific times and places. We lost the money invested, *plus* half the year's profits. The strike lasted two months. In November of that year, I was forced into bankruptcy. We lost everything. The chain reaction from that horrendous loss was a terrible grinding ordeal.

This incident taught me two things. (1) Labor problems can hurt innocent bystanders, and (2) they can come abruptly without warning — overnight in my case. Fortunately, we had stored some grain and canned goods, which helped us immensely during the difficult months ahead.

Labor and Food

In the mid Seventies, a number of labor contracts come up for renewal. Because of the terribly high inflation rate and loss of purchasing power, (12.5% in 1973) many unions are expected to demand 20% to 30% increases in pay and benefits. Management will dig in their heels, and strikes are inevitable — violent, stubborn, prolonged, dirty strikes.

Which unions could upset food distribution and production?

The Knights of the Road

During the gas and diesel fuel crunch during the winter of 1973-74, truckers protested high fuel prices, low allocations and lower speed limits. They blocked freeways, truck stops and loading docks with their rigs. Drivers who didn't want to strike were beaten up, and shot at by snipers. Later, a group of independent truckers called for a general strike on May 13, 1974. It wasn't successful — that time. Their timing was wrong. They were between shortages, as things had eased temporarily and fuel was freely available. The truckers' resentment is still simmering due to continued high fuel prices and low speed limits. The fuel shortages will come again — over and over several times until the great depression stops everything. What happens next time? Will the truckers strike in protest?

If they do, what happens to our food supplies?

I can see nothing but panic and empty supermarket shelves. If it happens at the wrong time, I see perishable foods rotting in the field. I see foods rotting in trucks, stopped at blockaded fuel pumps. Crops won't get to processors. Processors won't have containers. I can't think of anything so destructive to our food supply. What are the odds? No bookie, knowing the facts, would be willing to cover a bet against it.

Farm Workers

For many years, farm workers had no voice, and no political power. Under the prodding of Cesar Chavez, they have become a powerful self-interest group. They have millions of sympathizers willing to carry out secondary boycotts, such as the table grape boycott of our supermarkets.

A second element introduced itself. Farmers and producers, frightened of Chavez's apparent radical views, and knowing unions were now inevitable, sought for a more "respectable" labor organization to deal with. The teamsters moved in, and Chavez lost large contracts to them. There has been, and will be, violence and vicious jurisdictional disputes. The man in the middle is the grower. The ultimate loser is the consumer. Inflation triggers greater labor demands. The grower faces skyrocketing costs for fertilizer, fuel and farm equipment, so he can't give in easily. (More about that later). If the teamster truckers strike, can the teamster farmworkers be far behind? (Or vice versa?) Increasing costs, coupled with strikes at harvest time, or planting time can snap a link in our fragile food chain.

What are the odds here? Much better than even, in favor of bad trouble. The casualty? Our food!

Other Weak Links

Strikes by unions representing meat packers, processors, retail grocery clerks, railroads, oil refineries, service stations, canneries, packaging, plastics, metals, fertilizers — all could trigger a panic.

More Danger Today

We've had labor problems in the past. Why is it any more of a threat to our food supply today?

1. Because of inflation! Inflation is a wild beast that ravages everything it touches. When the increase necessary to keep up with the cost of living was only 3% or 4%, contracts could be negotiated in an orderly manner, and strikes were *relatively* short lived and *relatively* civilized. But when the cost of living is going up 12% a year, or 15%, or 30%, negotiation becomes almost impossible. There is *no* civilized solution. All there can be is confrontation. It is fueled by fear of bankruptcy on the part of management. Products might be priced out of the market, in an attempt to recover costs, which means no sales. Labor and management are now playing leap frog, with higher wages, then higher prices to cover costs, then higher wages to keep up with the cost of living. This game of leapfrog is one no one wins, because there is no finish line, short of bankruptcy. (Which I guess is a finish line of sorts.)

2. Because of the energy shortage.

The energy crisis represents one of the greatest threats to our food situation, creating both short term and long term problems. Agriculture, container manufacturing, food processing and transportation all use huge supplies of energy.

Agriculture and Energy

The steps involved in the production of food seem to be nothing but a chain of weak links. The "Green

Revolution" of the 1960's was triggered by the development of new strains of wheat, corn and other grains which dramatically increased the yield per acre — as much as 100% in some cases. This great boon to mankind had one potentially murderous flaw. These new strains are not hardy and are totally dependent on good weather, pesticides and massive amounts of *synthetic fertilizers.* This green revolution was possible only because the world has been generally enjoying the best weather for growing for the last 15 years that has been seen in modern times. This has now ended. More about this in a later chapter. It is fertilizer that concerns me here. **The vast bulk of our commercial fertilizer is made from petroleum and natural gas.**

When it became evident that we were running out of petroleum, and our natural gas supplies were shaky, it was obvious that the farmer would be hit several ways. He wouldn't have enough fertilizer. The National Observer for March, 1974, quoted the Governor of Nebraska as saying his state would be 15 to 23% short of the fertilizer necessary for spring planting. This would drive up food prices, by reducing yields, while dramatically increasing the farmers' costs. The vulnerability of strains of corn and wheat now used would tend to further exaggerate the effects of the shortage. **Fertilizer shortage, bad weather, and vulnerable strains of grain — a deadly combination.**

Fuel costs for planting, cultivating, harvesting and drying crops have more than doubled.

Costs of farm machinery have gone out of sight, due in part to increasing energy costs.

The farmer could see forthcoming fuel shortages for shipping, trucking strikes, and the weather forecasts for a 3 to 8 year drought starting this year or next. This means uncertainty. The farmer cannot operate in a climate of uncertainty. He has to be able to see ahead from planting to harvest. If he can't, his tendency is to hold back on production — to play it safe.

Distribution and Energy

It has been said, in jest I think, that if you kicked a dinosaur in the tail, it wouldn't move for 30 seconds, because it takes that long for the message to get all the way from his tail to his dim brain, and for the information to be processed and translated into appropriate action. But when he acts, oh boy!

The American market place can be much the same. The daily papers, radio, T.V. and the news magazines have been full of the problems discussed here. The consumer has been kicked in the tail. Some time the message is going to hit the brain that the food supply of this country is vulnerable to our transportation problems, that a simple truck fuel shortage, or a truck strike triggered by fuel shortages and high fuel costs, would stop the flow of food into our cities. When the message finally hits the brain — oh boy! Watch out! You will see panic buying, as people realize "no trucks" means "no food".

An *imagined* truck strike or fuel shortage would have exactly the same impact as a real one. Even a rumor, if published widely, could trigger a stampede to the supermarket. Look what happened to toilet paper when Johnny Carson mentioned a shortage on his show. He was only kidding, but there was a panic anyway, and supplies didn't get back to normal for weeks.

During the early days of the Patty Hearst kidnapping, I found myself driving through Oakland past one of the distribution centers where food packages were being passed out according to the demands of the S.L.A. extortionists. A gang of young toughs had jumped onto the food truck and were throwing packages to the mob, including breakable containers. I watched food smashed and trampled, and people making five and six trips to their cars with armloads of groceries. There was panic, animal-like behavior, greed, screams and curses. It was scary. The only reason I stayed around was because I was stuck in the jammed-up traffic and couldn't leave. I was stuck there for the half hour it took to complete the carnage.

I had the panic feeling driven home in a more personal way when we had a meat shortage in late 1973 and the meat market counters were empty. I was in the local supermarket, walking past the meat counter, when a butcher dumped a cart load of ground beef packages into the bin. I reached to pick up one or two and was almost trampled in the rush, as every woman in the store swarmed over me and started grabbing meat. I was elbowed, kicked, kneed and generally roughed up. Catching the spirit of the occasion, I fought for my share. I got ten packages and headed for the check-out stand. Then the shock hit me as I realized what I had done. I had been caught up in mob panic. So I can understand how it can happen. Knowing that feeling, I don't want to be within a mile of a supermarket if a transportation problem cuts off urban food supplies!

Containers and Energy

Lorenzo Hoopes, an executive of Safeway stores, was interviewed early in 1974 for the financial section of the *San Francisco Chronicle.* He discussed at some length the problems of food supply, and dwelt on the problems of containers. He said, in effect, that it was possible to have food in the warehouses, but not in the stores, if there were no containers to put it in.

Substantial energy is used in the making of glass, cardboard, paper and metal for cans. Plastics are particularly vulnerable, as they are made from petroleum. In the last few years there has been massive movement towards plastic for packaging pastries, dairy products, cereals, meats, vegetables, fruits, etc. However, the Federal Energy Office has placed a low priority for allocation of petroleum to the petrochemical and plastics industries.

3. Increasing Militancy.

Throughout U.S. history, mass violence has been infrequent, despite what some people have claimed. No nation in history has had such orderly change and growth. Those that have resorted to violence have been a lunatic minority. *Until recently!* Today, tens of thousands are willing to man the barricades for their cause. Various racial, social, and economic groups have risen from the bottom of our society, to the middle layers, and they are carrying the resentments of their former low estate. But now they are acquiring wealth, power, and the attention of the media. Some just causes have been captured by hatemongers. They cleverly mix large doses of genuine social or economic injustice, with hate, revenge, and often, a self-righteous desire to impose their solutions on everyone by intimidation or violence. They have a wide range of motives, ranging from genuine social concern, to Messiah complexes, to international conspiracy, to a kind of charismatic paranoia. Add to this tinderbox the genuine grinding problems of skyrocketing living costs, increasing unemployment as businesses fail or cut back operations, and young activists fishing in the "Establishment's" troubled waters, and you have a potential severing of our food chain at any one of several weak points. Where will it come from first? I don't know, but it is a mathematical certainty — it will happen. The result — no food to buy, and very possibly, for a period of time at least, the end of our present order of things.

CHAPTER IV

Famine — at Home And Abroad

Famine is something that happens in India. I grew up believing that if I didn't eat everything on my plate, someone in India would die. Perhaps the time has come when I won't have that extra unwanted food on my plate — and someone in India will die anyway!

All the evidence seems to show there will be a world-wide famine in the 70's, and this time the United States will be caught up in it. The reasons?

1. Population growth abroad.
2. Increased exports, as our food is shipped overseas to save the starving.
3. Changing climate and reduced production.
4. International monetary crises.
5. No reserves in America.

Let's tackle them one at a time.

Population Growth Abroad

If world population continues to increase at the present rate, we will create a new population equal to that of the whole United States — every year. This is due to the birth rate and increased longevity.

Efforts to limit births by contraception and abortion are rejected by large parts of the world. In parts of India your wealth and prestige is measured by how many children you have. Religious practices, customs, etc., have been too much to overcome. Much of the world is Roman Catholic and rejects birth control.

But the biggest factor in the current population rate of increase is the fact that modern medicine has vastly increased the number of people who survive childhood and grow to maturity and live to a ripe old age.

The story is told of an English missionary doctor who spent years bringing medical care to a remote African Village. Before his arrival, only two of eight children survived to maturity. Due to immunization, insect control and modern medicine, eight out of ten children survived to maturity. When the doctor pointed with pride to this accomplishment, the Chief of the tribe said, "Wonderful! But who will feed them?" This has produced a population increase way beyond the birth rate alone.

As the population grows, the land available for cultivation shrinks. Large cities, which are usually located in the best places, on the best land, are growing rapidly and swallowing up potential crop land. For awhile this can be compensated for by scientifically increasing yields and bringing marginal lands into production.

But soon the developing country can't meet its own food needs and must import.

The U.S. has been the granary of the world, exporting grain, meeting our own needs and still having huge surpluses, which had to be bought by the Federal Government. These surpluses controlled prices, as the government could dump some on the market if it wanted to. It served as a cushion against a bad crop year, or a famine or drought abroad. And prices remained stable for many years.

In 1972 and 1973, a series of circumstances drastically altered this balance.

World Weather Problems

India, due to the "Green Revolution" and massive American aid, both financial and technical, reached a state of self-sufficiency in grain in 1968. This was a major triumph.

But some basic climatic changes in 1972 and 1973 wiped out this gain.

The world weather began to change. Weather scientists claim the earth's weather, moisture and temperature patterns are *returning to normal.* We have had extraordinary growing weather for the last 15 years. All the food production projections are based on the assumption that this would continue.

"Green Revolution" — A Fatal Mistake?

During the past few years when we should have been developing strains of cereal grains for hardiness, self-sufficiency, resistance to disease, cold, erratic weather and insect infestation, the scientists strove for yield and rapid growth, at the expense of hardiness and adaptability. As a result, the world is depending on grains that require good growing weather, adequate rain at the right time, massive amounts of pesticides, *and huge quantities of fertilizer.*

A hideous combination of problems began brewing in 1972 and 1973, and are continuing to accelerate and take their toll.

The Weather

TIME MAGAZINE
June 24, 1974 — The Science Section

ANOTHER ICE AGE?

"In Africa, drought continues for the sixth consecutive year, adding terribly to the toll of famine victims. During 1972 record rains in parts of the U.S., Pakistan and Japan caused some of the worst flooding in centuries. In Canada's wheat belt, a particularly chilly and rainy spring has delayed planting and may well bring a disappointingly small harvest. Rainy Britain, on the other hand, has suffered from uncharacteristic dry spells the past few springs. A series of unusually cold winters has gripped the American Far West, while New England and northern Europe have recently experienced the mildest winters within anyone's recollection.

"As they review the bizarre and unpredictable weather pattern of the past several years, a growing number of scientists are beginning to suspect that many seemingly contradictory meteorological fluctuations are actually part of a global climatic upheaval. However widely the weather varies from place to place and time to time, when meteorologists take an average of temperatures around the globe they find that the atmosphere has been growing gradually cooler for the past three decades. The trend shows no indication of reversing. Climatological Cassandras are becoming apprehensive, for the weather aberrations they are studying may be the harbinger of another ice age.

"Telltale signs are everywhere — from the unexpected persistence and thickness of pack ice in the waters around Iceland to the southward migration of a warmth-loving creature like the armadillo from the Midwest. Since the 1940's the mean global temperature has dropped about 2.7° F. Although that figure is at best an estimate, it is supported by other convincing data. When Climatologist George J. Kukla of Columbia University's Lamon-Doherty Geological Observatory and his wife Helena analyzed satellite weather data for the Northern Hemisphere, they found that the area of the ice and snow cover had suddenly increased by 12% in 1971 and the increase has persisted ever since. Areas of Baffin Island in the Canadian Arctic, for example, were once totally free of any snow in summer; now they are covered year round.

"Scientists have found other indications of global cooling. For one thing there has been a noticeable expansion of the great belt of dry, high-altitude polar winds — the so-called circumpolar vortex — that sweep from west to east around the the top and bottom of the world. Indeed it is the widening of this cap of cold air that is the immediate cause of Africa's drought. By blocking moisture-bearing equatorial winds and preventing them from bringing rainfall to the parched sub-Sahara region, as well as other drought-ridden areas stretching all the way from Central America to the Middle East and India, the polar winds have in effect caused the Sahara and other deserts to reach farther to the south. *Paradoxically, the same vortex has created quite different weather quirks in the U.S. and other temperature zones. As the winds swirl around the globe, their southerly portions undulate like the bottom of a skirt. Cold air is pulled down across the Western U.S. and warm air is swept up to the Northeast. The collision of air masses of widely differing temperatures and humidity can create violent storms – the Midwest's recent rash of disastrous tornadoes, for example.*

"Whatever the cause of the cooling trend, its effects could be extremely serious, if not catastrophic. . . .

"The earth's current climate is something of an anomaly. In the past 700,000 years, there have been at least seven major episodes of glaciers spreading over much of the planet. Temperatures have been as high as they are now only about 5% of the time. *But there is a peril more immediate than the prospect of another ice age.* Even if temperature and rainfall patterns change only slightly in the near future in one or more of the three major grain-exporting countries — the U.S., Canada and Australia — global food stores would be sharply reduced. University of Toronto Climatologist Kenneth Hare, a former president of the Royal Meteorological Society, believes that the continuing drought and the recent failure of the Russian harvest gave the world a grim premonition of what might happen. Warns Hare: "*I don't believe that the world's present population is sustainable if there are more than three years like 1972 in a row.*' "

Balance of Payments

One bad dry year in Russia and India in 1972 upset the entire equation. Both India and Russia had to buy huge quantities of grain from us and Canada. This fit right into our government's plans, as the dollar had weakened tremendously in the international money markets, due partly to a huge balance-of-payments deficit. (Imports exceeding exports, which sends too many dollars overseas). This could be turned around overnight by exporting our huge food reserves. Famine abroad was good for America!

War between India and Pakistan created famine. The worst floods in history hit Pakistan and Bangladesh. In Africa, the Sahara Desert was marching south at an increasing rate. And then, the Arab-Israeli war dealt the world a terrible blow!

Oil and Famine — The Commodity War

The Arab oil-producing nations, in a rare show of unity, decided to use their vast oil reserves to influence the U.S. and other countries to drop support of Israel. They increased the world price of oil to the point where the poorer nations, which needed oil the most for development, could not pay for it. Other oil-producing nations followed suit. Transportation was disrupted, a great fertilizer shortage developed, and the world's misery was compounded.

The world knuckled under to the Arabs. In the U.S., environmentalists had halted the Alaskan pipeline, offshore drilling, coal strip-mining, and nuclear plant construction. Japan's economy began to grind to a halt, while inflation rates there soared past 20%. And the world's money ($80 billion in 1974) began to pour into the coffers of a few tiny nations, resulting in a world-wide capital shortage. World-wide inflation made the Arabs cautious about making their money available for investment or loans to developing nations with poor credit, who were the hardest hit.

Commodity Blackmail

Now, a very small tail was wagging a very large dog. This lesson was not lost on other small nations who controlled critical commodities. Jamaica, one of the world's largest producers of bauxite (aluminum ore) increased their royalty from $2.00 to $11.00 a ton — a sudden 450% increase! Other nations are following suit, thus fueling the fires of inflation.

America — The Empty Granary

Now, the world was poised for a disaster of epic proportions. *We were dependent on vulnerable grains.* Drought, war, and floods caused widespread crop destruction. Fertilizer was soaring in cost and becoming unavailable, the population was exploding, capital was short. Where could the world turn for help? To the U.S.?

Our reserves were gone!

For awhile it looked as we could take up the slack. Officials predicted the largest wheat and corn crop in history in 1974. We had more land under cultivation than ever before. We had planted more than ever before. Soaring food prices had increased the farmer's incentive, and he was more prosperous than he had been for years.

But as this is written, everything is going sour. What happened?

An Outraged Nature

When the winter wheat crop harvest began, the expected yields simply were not materializing. Much of the new land under cultivation was marginal. Fuel shortages abounded. But the weather had gone crazy!

On Tuesday, June 11, the *San Francisco Chronicle* reported —

WEATHER REDUCES WHEAT ESTIMATE

Washington:

Dry weather, disease and hail damage in the Great Plains have put a dent in the expected winter wheat harvest which accounts for about three-fourths of the nation's bread grain, the Agriculture department reported yesterday.

Winter wheat comprises about three-fourths of the nation's bread grain and is the kind most in demand for export. Kansas, the leading producer, was estimated (on June 10 — author) to produce 384.2 million bushels. On *May 8* the department had forecast the state's crop at 406.8 million.

But grain officials in Kansas said the new USDA estimate is still too high. Drought and disease damage has been widespread, one official said, and the state may produce only 300 million bushels this year.

"I still think it is too high", Creel Brock, administrator of the Kansas Wheat Commission, said in a telephone interview. "We're going to stick with the 300 million bushels yet for a while".

Last month the department's Kansas wheat estimate was attacked by many grain authorities and farmers in the state as being inflated.

Although USDA field estimates for

> spring-planted wheat will not be made until July the reduced prospects for winter grain means the United States may have less total wheat for export and domestic consumption during 1974-75 than expected earlier.
>
> Heavy usage, including record exports, is expected to drain the present old-crop reserve to a 27-year low of 170 million bushels by this July 1.

In Idaho, Friday June 14, 1974, was designated as a day of prayer for the wheat and hay crops, due to drought and high spring winds.

Corn, however, was suffering from the opposite problem. *Too much rain* further north in the corn belt has turned the 1974 crop into a disaster.

The Wall Street Journal, Tuesday, June 18, 1974, reported:

> "That 6.7 billion-bushel corn crop you've heard Agriculture Secretary Earl L. Butz talking about has been cancelled because of rain.
>
> "Delayed planting, dilution of fertilizer by standing water, erosion of topsoil, marginal land in production falling way short of expectation. This means increased animal protein costs and depressed farm and ranch economies."

Then came the Drought!

The Department of Agriculture issued periodic reports all during the summer of 1974 on the grain crop status, as a searing drought spread further and further in mid-America. Farmers began to cut corn early, to save it for silage. In some areas wheat was plowed under and fields replanted with soybeans. As pastures dried out, ranchers began selling underweight cattle, to salvage something from the disaster. Every Midwest state but Indiana asked for disaster aid.

Finally, on August 12, the Agriculture Department half admitted the extent of the disaster. Rather than the forecast record yields, corn would be 12 to 20 percent *below* last year, and that included silage! Soybeans were way down. Wheat was still estimated to be 7% above 1973, but they were expecting 27% and all the wheat figures weren't in yet.

The best possible prediction anyone could make for the food situation was to forecast much higher food prices, starting in the fall of 1974, for meat and grains, and spot shortages. By fall of 1974, the food suppliers told me of a massive scramble to secure supplies for processing and stockpiling, with purchases being made as far away as Argentine, Australia, and Taiwan.

And all our reserves had been sold abroad! And demand was increasing at home.

Just A Passing Problem?

All the evidence indicates this bizarre weather in America is just the beginning of a major weather cycle. We're not talking about the monsoons of Southeast Asia or the Sahara Desert, but America! Here!

We're not talking about just one bad year! This is the first of 3 to 8 such years!

In March of 1974, every major newspaper and news magazine carried some predictions of the drought.

U.S. NEWS AND WORLD REPORT
March 18,1974

"WILL WIDESPREAD DROUGHT HIT THE COUNTRY SOON?"

(An Interview with Weather Scientist, Walter O. Roberts)

> . . . "If you look at the past history of the high plains, by which I mean the the first 600 to 800 miles east of the Rockies, the evidence is pretty conclusive that there have been something like eight successive serious dry periods spaced approximately 20 to 23 years apart. . . .
>
> . . . "Therefore, I personally am watching very intently for a drought in the mid-1970's in the high plains. . . .
>
> . . . "We would expect a drought beginning either this spring or the following spring. *And the drought we would expect should last anywhere from three to eight years,* (emphasis mine) judging from past droughts in this particular series".

THE NATIONAL OBSERVER
March 30, 1974

"THE NEXT CRISIS: UNIVERSAL FAMINE"

"A catastrophic world famine has suddenly become possible again. The prospect of wide-spread starvation has had more serious political and scientific attention in recent months that it has received in years. This time the doomsayers aren't just talking again about squalor in India, but also about shortages, high prices, and maybe even food rationing in the U.S.

". . . First, the enormous American agricultural surplus that used to prevent famines elsewhere has entirely vanished. The last grains of wheat or oats or whatever were sold off from Government bins last summer.

. . . "Against this background of high prices, short supplies, and the evaporation of surplus Government food stocks, the prospect of even a minor crop failure scares the daylights out of politicians and food experts.

. . . "Fertilizer prices have doubled to tripled in the past year or so. The Governor of Nebraska says there is a 15 to 23 percent shortage in his state.

. . . "Even at the generally optimistic Department of Agriculture, one finds occasional bubbles of middle-level speculation over the "moral necessity" of food rationing in this country if "extraordinary" food shortage occurs in the rest of the world.

NEWSWEEK
April 1, 1974

"RUNNING OUT OF FOOD"

". . . Even a mild drought in this tight supply situation", said one Agriculture Department official, "could be a disaster".

Reserves Gone!

Like Old Mother Hubbard, our cupboard is bare. We're like a family that is living well by spending all their income. Everything is great, as long as our income continues. But if the income is cut off for a few weeks, or suddenly reduced, we're in trouble. If we have savings, they will tide us over. But if our savings have been spent, foolishly invested or loaned, we go hungry.

With no reserves to cushion us, we could be as hungry as India. We have huge export committments. If we cut our exports, we trigger more commodity black-mail in retaliation, and increase our balance-of-payments deficit, damaging the dollar and increasing the rate of debasement of our currency. Even during the height of the Arab oil boycott, we still shipped the Arabs the usual amounts of food, attesting to the power of commodity blackmail. Also, don't forget that we have huge industrial (non-food) uses for our crops. Our reserves are down to

23 days as of this writing. We face a dwindling supply. An increasing demand, and possible permanent weather changes — and no cushion to protect us.

If the experts are right about our climate, the earth will never be the same again. All over the world, tens of millions of people will die. In this country, there will be a wild scramble for food, and food will have to be rationed.

Rationing

Politicians have been making statements recently about the "moral necessity" of reducing our food consumption here so we can help poorer nations. This means two things — rationing or allocation. Hubert Humphrey said, on a television special on the food crisis, that a nation whose major health problem was obesity had to face the fact that we could do with less food here, to send food abroad.

With all the clouds over our head, I am not prepared to depend on our government to be efficient, prudent, wise, timely, or fair, in seeing that everyone has their fair share of food. The only truly dependable food source for me will be what I can personally produce or store. I'm not a farmer, I have a big family, and only my one-acre home lot for growing, so I will have to depend primarily on what I can store now.

CHAPTER V

Prudent Storage or Hoarding?

W. Cleon Skousen, a noted writer and educator, and former Chief of Police of Salt Lake City, made a profound statement to me regarding the morality of storing food.

"If you buy up food when there is plenty, that's food storage. If you wait until it's scarce, that's hoarding".

As of this writing there is plenty of food readily available (albeit at rapidly increasing prices), as the impact of all the problems is not really being felt yet.

The time to start your storage program is now! Because of rising prices it is already too late for many! But you must do it right! In later chapters we'll show you how. But you must be responsible for your own family. Don't wait until the crisis is so obvious that everyone is scrambling for food. Begin an orderly, systematic, well-planned storage program immediately.

How to Buy

By all means, if you have the money, buy your whole

program now — at least a one-year supply for each member of the family. If you don't have the money, start making some sacrifices and buy systematically each month as much as you can, and hope you didn't start too late.

How About Borrowing?

I start with a bias against borrowing for my food supplies because my Church leaders have drummed into me the principle of debt avoidance, and have said specifically in regard to food storage, "We do not advocate going into debt". If you are not of my religious persuasion, you will make your decision on other grounds. If you are a Mormon without a storage program, due to your procrastination, you are caught between your church leaders' counsel on debt, and their counsel on storage. You might consider the following points.

The high rate of inflation, including food costs, may make it impossible for you if you wait. You may have to pay the price of your procrastination by financing your storage program. If you do, observe the following precautions:

1. Make the largest down payment possible and pay it off as fast as you can. The interest will be off-set by the savings by buying at today's prices.

2. Be sure the payments can be met from your budget, allowing for the inflation of all your other costs. This means also a reasonable assurance that your employment is secure, and your income will continue over the life of the loan. If you default, your investment would

be lost, and your food could be repossessed.

3. Obtain a "Creditor Life" Insurance policy on the loan, so that the death of the bread-winner would not result in the loss of the food supply, just when it is needed most by the family.

4. Be sure that your food has an adequate shelf life, so that it's still good when it's paid for.

5. Don't borrow to meet current expenses, or to finance *depreciating* goods such as T.V. sets, furniture, etc. Your food supply, however, is an *appreciating* asset, increasing in value every day. It is excellent collateral.

But, again — if you must finance, make the largest down payment possible, and pay it off as soon as possible, making whatever sacrifices are necessary.

A Medium of Exchange

We made reference in earlier chapters to the value of food for barter, or as a medium of exchange if our currency collapses. This argues for properly prepared, concentrated foods. You should be willing, if necessary, to pay a substantial premium for the best possible packaging in small units, so it is durable, transportable, and convenient for exchange. This is, of course, after meeting your own family survival requirements.

CHAPTER VI

The Crystal Ball

The best way to become a false prophet is to set a date for the end of the world and get it wrong. I don't have a crystal ball, and I don't *know* whether we have weeks, months, or years to prepare. But I think I can forecast *what* to expect with a fair degree of accuracy, and I will share my opinions with you as to the order in which things will happen, and the general periods in which these calamities become more likely. So, here goes!

Short Term Problems

I firmly believe we will have a series of short term food emergencies, some of them sudden, caused by labor or transportation problems. A sudden strike, a food buying panic for a few days, then an apparent easing of the problem, while everyone breathes a sigh of relief at the "false alarm", as things seem to return to normal. The only evidence of the problem will be a permanent upward spurt in food prices.

This will repeat itself at intervals, each time a little worse, each time requiring you to be dependent on your food supplies for longer periods of time.

How soon these problems start depends to a great degree on government policy on exports. Strangely enough, as *our* problems with food become more dangerous, more politicians are talking about *more* exports, not less, because of the "moral necessity" to help the world, and our balance of payments problem.

An analogy might be our gas shortage. In the summer of 1973, for a few short days, we found some stations were limiting purchases to ten gallons, or running out in the late afternoon. Then things got better, everyone assumed the problem was over. Then in the winter of '73-'74; a worse crunch hit, and we all spent hours in gas lines. Then it got better again, and as this is written, I can buy all the gas I want — at higher prices, of course; as this was "necessary" to stimulate oil companies to produce more gas. Shortages will come again — and again — a little worse each time, until the automobile is no longer a viable means of transportation, as it cannot be depended upon.

The same pattern is developing with food. In my area, in '73 and '74 we have seen a brief meat shortage — twice, and a brief milk shortage, and a brief bread shortage. I have never seen any shortages in my lifetime, except during World War II — until now. This, during record crop years! Then came the meat glut, caused by high meat prices stimulating over-production. This will be followed by the meat shortage — a little worse next time, as the glut forces prices down at the farm level, and farmers are caught in feed grain price squeezes due to weather-caused shortages, etc., thus diminishing production, causing bankruptcies among ranchers and feed lot operators. Each time this happens you will need your food storage for a little while.

A Personal Famine

Inflation and recession will cause increased unemployment; and if you are vulnerable to an interruption of income, you could have your own *personal* famine.

I am grateful for the food we had stored in 1968 when we lost our assets, our income and our credit as a result of my business failure.

Each time one of these short term problems occurs, there will be a rush to food storage, and prices will jump, and it will be harder to store.

Victims Of Their Own Success

During the 1973-74 gas shortage, the food storage companies had such an increase in business that some of them were not able to deliver all the food they sold, due to shortages and lack of facilities. In some instances they were under-capitalized to meet the demand for expansion, so they took the customer's money, which he had paid for undelivered food, and let him wait while they spent it to expand production facilities. Then the gas situation improved, the public relaxed, sales and cash flow dropped just long enough that they didn't have the cash to deliver the back-ordered food. The delay in delivery embarrassed their salesmen, so many of them quit, further reducing volume. One of the two largest companies in the field filed bankruptcy just a few weeks before publication, and others are in shaky condition.

When to Buy

This "panic buying — complacency" cycle will continue for awhile. **You must buy between Panics.** One fine food company has a great motto, worthy of note:

"It wasn't raining when Noah built the ark".

In short — there will be a recurring pattern of temporary food shortages and buying panics, each one worse than the one before, punctuated by periods of complacency and apparent food sufficiency.

No one wants to believe things will change for the worse. No one wants to believe the "Prophets of Doom and Gloom". No administration wants to be pessimistic, or look bad. Optimistic government statements and forecasts prevent panic buying, force down commodity prices, and get incumbents re-elected. And the public co-operates by not wanting to hear the nasty truth, and tends to believe the best, until they get scared.

Long Term Problems

The Weather

As we have already shown, it appears to be permanently changing for the worse. This not only means not enough food, but disruption of the economy of large segments of the United States. It will take years to adapt.

How soon will this mean living off your storage? **As**

soon as the American mass consumer wakes and starts buying food. This could happen anytime. It could be triggered by a television special, a presidential speech, a bill in Congress authorizing stand-by food rationing powers, more spot shortages — the right jolt at the right time. It may have happened by the time you read this book.

The door will slam shut when the Government sees the panic-buying starting, and simply moves massively and swiftly into the marketplace and buys up all reserves of food, ostensibly to "prevent panic buying", but really to be sure the Armed Forces are fed, and to preserve its ability to function. Past agricultural buying programs have given the Federal Government both the machinery and the authority to do this quickly.

The Economy

Banking collapse, stock market collapse, international monetary problems, a sharp spurt in an already ruinous inflation rate — any of these things could occur at any time, and cripple our society for years to come. No one knows how much resilience there is in our economy, or how many insults it can endure; but when the break comes, it will be sudden, devastating, and last for years.

You Bet Your Life

The only definite timetable I can give you is — Do It Now. Anything else is potentially suicidal. You are betting your life and that of your family. If you bet against me by not preparing and I'm right, you lose! You're hungry! If you bet with me and prepare now, and I'm wrong, the worst thing that can happen to you is that you will have made an excellent investment — saved a lot of money, as the long term trend of food prices is definitely up dramatically.

Could Howard Ruff Be Wrong?

Could I be wrong?

Of course I could be — if you can change the world weather, stop the birth rate, reduce the lifespan, invent new cereal grains this week, repeal all the economic laws, and teach the Arabs to love the Jews.

I *could* be wrong as to the *sequence* of events. I *could* be wrong on timing. But don't bet your life against me. Remember, if you bet against me, you have everything to lose and nothing to gain. Bet with me, and you have everything to gain and nothing to lose.

As Robert Preston says, "Better a year too soon, than a day too late".

CHAPTER VII

I'd Give Anything To Be Wrong

Even as I write this, I recoil from the sheer necessity for such a book. From the time I first put pen to paper, I've been flying in the face of my personal inclinations.

I think the reason I wasn't enthusiastic about food storage until recently was a compound of procrastination, lack of knowledge, and just plain lack of interest. Any storage we had was the work of my wife. I find it difficult to see bad things ahead. So this has been a painful effort.

I have forced myself to examine my conclusions, and I don't enjoy the implications, so I can understand if you reject my ideas out of hand. Just be sure that your rejection is based on data as good as mine, not just on inability to cope emotionally with the facts.

Here are the implications you must face.

1. If I am right, our society, as we know it will change, and life will be different for all of us.

2. Our plans for the future must be completely rearranged. Our savings, our retirement plans, our jobs,

even our physical safety is in jeopardy.

3. We will be faced, if we prepare properly, with coping with the problems of eating in a starving world. We will have to protect our family's security, while others, not so prudent, are suffering.

4. All the idealistic values, which are quite easy to defend in an orderly world, will be challenged. We will face the hard questions of whether or not we will share our means with others, if this means our children suffer.

5. All our wonderful plans for our children, such as college, to become doctors or lawyers, etc. may be in jeopardy, because they require an orderly world.

Does this outlook have to be so dark?

Let me give you a few rays of light to relieve the gloom.

The Silver Lining

When the collapse occurs, it will be a temporary condition. Our land is rich in resources, knowledge and energy. I don't think we can avoid the crash, but we can recover from it. I *don't* see a new "Dark Age" lasting for centuries. I see a chaotic period of one to five years. Out of the chaos, a new group of leaders will arise. Those who have prepared properly and survived will step forward and bring order. Those who demonstrated the foresight to prepare will be looked to for leadership.

The Constitution

The groups of people who are now preparing for the crash seem to be those who are the strongest supporters of Constitutional government, personal freedom, and sound currency. I believe that the new order will be founded on the same principles of freedom our forefathers envisioned, because they who survive will be the ones who believe in those principles. Because of their understanding of sound principles they are the ones who have seen this crisis coming.

Permanent Change

When the recovery comes, there will have been changes wrought in our system and life style that will be permanent features of our society.

The Weather.

If the meteorologists are right, there will be a definite shifting of economic factors from one part of the country to another. The corn belt and the wheat belt will shift position. Changing temperature, rainfall and season lengths will alter economic patterns.

The World Economy.

If world wide inflation, drought, and political upheaval cause the millions of deaths we anticipate, many parts of the world will sink into the stone age. It is estimated that in Africa seven to eleven million people will die in 1974 due to drought. The Sahara Desert is moving south, and the Northern Sahara may become fertile again. The changes in world trade wrought by such shifts could be incalculable. We could cease to be an exporting country, due to the world's inability to pay, and our own shortages.

The U.S. Economy.

With a collapse in the currency, many of the rich will become poor. The producers of food and other necessities will rise to the top of the heap. Savings will be wiped out. The superstructure of a swollen government bureaucracy will collapse and the maze of government regulatory rules will simply wither as they mean nothing, because there will be nothing to regulate. The new leadership will have a clean slate to write on, the mistakes of the past as an example, and a perfect opportunity to make a saner, better world.

World Population.

We will learn how delicately balanced the world's distribution and communication systems are, and as *Newsweek* has said:

"We will be seeing people starving to death on T.V. on the 10:00 news".

If there is T.V., or a 10:00 news!

Tens of millions of people dying will leave a less populous world. Out of this uncomprehendable tragedy will come a world population that can be supported by this planet.

Divine Destiny

I believe with all my heart that God has a plan for this world, but that he very seldom repeals natural law. Man will suffer the consequences of ignoring both God's laws, and the laws of nature and economics.

There can be no stability in a nation that forgets that

the basic unit of society is the home, and when a significant portion of our people either lose faith in it, or violate and reject the Eternal Laws that secure the family and hold it together, then a society comes apart as its smallest unit disintegrates. We will learn this the hard way as only the tightly knit families that are emotionally, physically and spiritually prepared will survive in good condition.

You can't indefinitely violate economic laws without weakening an economic structure. You can't penalize producers and sources of capital by confiscatory taxation, and crippling, expensive, unnecessary regulation, without eventually destroying any free economic system.

A Brave New World?

I've often been asked what I would do if my neighbors came to steal my food. Would I shoot them? I've given long thought to this question, and I've come up with the following answers.

1. I'm storing enough for my family and my relatives, and some extra for barter and to share with others, to the limit of my ability to do so.

2. I'm persuading my neighbors to build their own storage program, so they will be able to take care of themselves.

3. I'm preparing to protect my supplies by concealment and defensive arms from those who would take it by force. If necessary, I would attempt to defend myself and my family against marauding bands.

4. I'm allying myself with a strong community of like-minded individuals so we will be strong enough to

impose order on our area, if necessary. (Not a vigilante committee. We will function only if law disappears completely.)

5. I'm trying to live my life so I will be entitled to guidance from my Heavenly Father.

Getting Ready?

Here are a few miscellaneous suggestions to help you.

1. Get any corrective surgery and dental work done now.
2. Have someone in your family learn to sew, and stock durable fabrics for the family.
3. Stock up on shoes for everyone.
4. Consider a properly vented underground gas storage tank.
5. Collect books on outdoor survival, camp cooking, carpentry, mechanics, gardening, home first aid, etc.
6. Have a good supply of tools for car, garden, and kitchen.
7. Stock up on necessary medicines.
8. Lay in a good store of charcoal, and a grill, or other suitable fuel for cooking, such as coal, propane, butane or wood.
9. Have an effective family organization that is aware of the oncoming problem and prepared to be smoothly functioning parts of a machine that operates independently of the outside world.
10. Begin to build up health and physical condition now. Cut the junk foods out of your diet. Begin to de-

pend on basic foods. Start a regular exercise program to strengthen your body and increase its efficiency.

11. Begin a program of supplemental nutrition now to build your nutritional status. My family is so accustomed to using our supplements, our protein concentrates, and whole wheat dishes, that a shift to a complete storage program would simply mean less meat, and dehydrated vegetables and fruit instead of fresh.

12. Have a trial run. Live for a week on your storage program. You will quickly find out if you have a satisfactory one.

13. Be sure every member of the family understands the first part of this book and is emotionally ready for such a time.

What If It Never Happens?

What if I have misinterpreted the facts, and there is no collapse, our weather problems are only temporary, and science develops an unlimited source of protein.

What if our system is strong enough to withstand the shocks, and a benevolent Deity overlooks our collective sins. I believe that if this is the case, (and I desperately hope in my heart it is, despite the overwhelming evidence) the consequences of having prepared for a collapse can be nothing but good. I see the benefits as follows:

1. **An Excellent Investment.** The *present* shortages of food argue for increased inflation in food prices. All the experts are in agreement on that. The food you stockpile now will save you a great deal of money later. It

will never be this cheap again! I know of many who are buying food strictly as an investment. Properly prepared for long term storage, it is the one thing that is sure to increase in value. If you put $1,000 in the bank at 6%, and $1,000 in food, and left the country for one year, when you came back, which would have the most value, if we merely continue our present (June 1974) inflation rate of 13%? Your bank deposit will have lost value, and your food would have increased in value. The cost of food is rising at about double the rate of the cost of most everything else, and this will accelerate as the weather gets worse, and real shortages develop.

2. **Family Unity.** The very act of preparing as a family can strengthen our family life. It never hurts to prepare for self-sufficiency. We feel like a close knit unit.

3. **Improved Health.** As we have shifted our diet towards our food storage program, we've never been so healthy. As we shift from junk processed foods to more reliance on our concentrates, and basic foods, we have a tremendous sense of well-being and boundless energy.

4. **Peace of Mind.** Most of you have Life Insurance, Actually it should be called "Death Insurance". When you buy it, you are betting you will die during the life of the policy. If you are right, you win! You die! If you buy food insurance, you are betting you will need it. If you are right, you win! You live! If you are wrong, you win! You have better health, a stronger family, and a sense of security that enables you to look at the terrible trends, the frightening newspaper articles, all the bad news, with a peaceful feeling. You can say,

"I'm ready".

Your Response

As you go on to Part II, you can have one of four responses to what you have read so far.

1. You can dismiss it as the paranoid imagining of one of the calamity mongers and consider me a "Prophet of Doom and Gloom". If you do, I am sorry, for I will have failed with you. Perhaps a better writer might have succeeded. Of course, then you will do nothing to prepare, and you may as well not go on to Part II.

2. You can believe, but feel so overwhelmed by the facts, that you feel there is nothing you can do, so you cower in the corner, paralyzed with fear. In that case, please go on to Part II and III, and I will try to change your mind.

3. You can believe, go on to Part II and III, and through lethargy, or an unwillingness to make the necessary sacrifices, or just because of procrastination, do nothing until, it's too late.

Or,

4. You can believe, and from this moment on resolve to systematically begin to prepare. Man has gone through low cycles in history over and over. The strong and the mature, who were prepared, faced the future, and survived the troubles without fear. Calamities are times of growth for us all. I remember a profound statement made by one of my children, as we were talking at the dinner table about the effects of my business failure five years earlier. I had told them about a wealthy family I had visited, where the teenage daughter had a Porsche, a power boat, and a four hundred a week allowance.

There was a moment of stunned silence, and my 13 year old daughter said,

"The poor girl! I'm glad we lost *our* money before it did us any permanent harm".

She had recognized one great Eternal Truth. Adversity strengthens us, if we rise to the challenge. We as a family were stronger, closer, and more spiritual because of our reverses. Our loss was our gain.

Perhaps, we will rise from the ashes, cleansed and strengthened.

So be of good cheer, prepare well, and be ready to face a changed world with confidence and inner peace.

CHAPTER VIII

The Sacred Four

I have been personally disturbed over the bad advice that people have been given about food storage, most of it sincere and well-intended.

During normal times, when we can just run down to the supermarket whenever we want some food, it is possible to be reasonably well-nourished by accident, if we just eat a wide variety of quality foods. This is particularly true of protein. However, during a famine, if it is prolonged, all we will have to eat will be what we have stored. We can't store everything, so we must select carefully. We can't erase our mistakes and start over. We will live or die, be healthy or sick, based on the decisions we make now.

Wheat and Powdered Milk

Over the years the feeling developed among some that you could live in good health on wheat, powdered milk, honey and salt *alone.* This advice would be fine, except for the word "*alone*". It has given rise to the first of the "Deadly Myths".

This misconception among the Mormons stems partly from a section of the "Doctrine and Covenants", believed by Mormons to be a modern revelation, which gives some dietary rules and states "wheat for man". This statement evolved into a general feeling that wheat *alone* could be sufficient, which is not what the book says. Later, books such as *"Passport to Survival"* by Esther Dickey developed this theme and the "Basic Four" — wheat, powdered milk, honey, and salt — were announced as adequate for healthy survival. (Incidentally, Mrs. Dickey's book, except for this misconception, is outstanding as a general guide, and belongs in every library.)

This erroneous conclusion is based on some generally true and accepted principles, *from which some wrong conclusions have been drawn,* based on the following reasoning.

1. Proteins are made of amino acids. The value of a protein is determined by its amino acid profile. There are 8 which are considered essential.

2. If all eight essential amino acids are present, it is considered a "complete" protein.

3. Your body cannot make protein tissues, (such as muscle, skin, hair, lungs, heart, brain, enzymes, hormones, digestive fluids, etc.), out of your food, unless all 8 essential amino acids are present, *at the same time, in the same meal.*

4. Some foods have all the essential amino acids and are technically, "complete" proteins, but are *low* in one or more them. The body, then has only limited use of the other amino acids.

5. Wheat is about 12% protein, but is low in lysine,

one of the essential amino acids. In fact, lysine is considered super-essential in that it is one of the "limiting" amino acids. If a food is even a little low in lysine, according to John J. Miller, Ph.D., it can

> . . . "make practically worthless the other seven acids at the site of protein formation. The other seven amino acids are, of course, also essential, but a considerable decline in their availability could be countenanced without loss of all protein development. On the other hand, whereas a small increase in lysine availability would be wonderfully beneficial, a small deficit would be disastrous".

6. Milk has a fine amino acid profile, including extra lysine, and when taken with wheat, in the same meal, provides the necessary lysine to complete the amino acid profile for wheat, thus turning it into a complete well-balanced protein.

Where is the Error?

Wheat is a fine food. I have over a ton of it stored. Powdered milk is also useful. They have their place, but they have had qualities attributed to them which they don't really have, and therefore have some serious limitations.

First of all, why can't they provide the necessary protein?

Because there are some critical facts missing from the above logic.

The "wheat-powdered milk" theory is based on the assumption that whole *raw* milk and powdered skim milk have the same value. My studies have caused me to believe that **this is not true.** It was believed that modern processing methods used sufficiently low temperatures (spray drying as opposed to roller drying) to avoid damage to the amino acids. Chemical evaluations tend to bear this out, showing very little destruction of lysine. But here's the catch! **Even though the chemical analysis looks O.K., experimental animals die when forced to depend on these foods, but they thrive on the raw milk.**

Lysine and Milk Sugar

An experiment was conducted by two research teams under Dr. Lloyd Riggs and the results published in the *Journal of Agricultural Food Chemistry* (V. 3, No. 4, p. 333, 1955). The subject was lysine availability in food products.

> "One group of his laboratory assistants (Group I) was analyzing certain samples of milk solids, to determine the lysine content, and therefore their biological values. Another group of assistants (Group II) was testing the same foods as ingredients of a diet which should provide maximum growth for laboratory animals.
>
> "The milk solids (i.e. whey powder) were heated in Group I experiment to make them palatable for human consumption and then the usual chemical test for lysine was made,

and reported as practically 100% present. In the experiment by Group II, however, the *raw* whey powder was fed to animals and the growth rate was satisfactory.

Then the *heated* product from Group I test was fed to a similar group of animals with the result that *all the animals died.* The surprise was alarming to all concerned, because heated whey powder was to be fed in large amounts to animals as well as to humans throughout the Nation.

The question which faced Dr. Riggs was: Why did the lysine show up properly in the chemical test — even after heating the whey powder — and yet not be of value for animals. Finally the two groups of researchers got together and compared notes. The chemists of Group I insisted that the lysine had not been destroyed by heat such as food ordinarily stands, whereas Group II insisted that the lysine was not available to the animals. As the director of Group II remarked: 'If you think your chemical tests for availability are good, teach my animals to read your figures!'

As Dr. Riggs explained later, "*The heating of the whey forces a combination of lysine with the sugars of the whey, which did not spoil the chemical test, but "inactivated" the lysine content as far as nutrition of animals was concerned.*

'This same inactivation occurs of course in the human diet when lysine of cereal grains, of

> milk, soybeans, vegetables and even meats is made biologically unavailable by sterilization and other heating processes.
>
> "When milk is heated (as in canning or powdering) the sugars of milk combine with the lysine; also, in the preparation of babies' formulas wherein extra sugar or syrup is added and then the total product sterilized, the result is a serious loss of lysine values. Dependence upon such foods could mean a poor start in life for millions of babies through the United States".

The interesting thing about this study is that low temperature processes were used, supposedly well within the limits thought safe for milk. High temperatures would have shown actual destruction of lysine, which was not the case in this instance.

This phenomenon involving sugar and lysine is discussed by Robert S. Harris, Ph.D. (now with the Food and Drug Administration and Harry Von Loesecke, S.B. in their classic text "*Nutritional Evaluation of Food Processing*" (VI Publishing Co., Westport, Conn. 1971) p. 233. I'll spare you the scientific text, but their conclusion was that lysine and sugars combine in the presence of heat and even though lysine could be recovered with standard tests, "lysine may become biologically unavailable *in the absence of demonstrable destruction*".

Enzymes and Lysine

Harris and Loesecke also reveal a second problem

relating to the enzymes found in milk and wheat which appear to be necessary to make the protein available to the body.

One of the major purposes of pasteurization is to destroy or inactivate the enzymes found in milk, in order to stabilize flavors.

> ". . . Heat-induced enzyme destruction or inactivation is desirable in milk pasteurization. . . (enzymes) all may produce undesirable changes in milk and are naturally present in milk. . . . The enzyme-catalyzed changes are generally objectionable from the point of altered flavor alone, since flavor alteration usually means a decreased consumption of the milk product with a consequent reduced intake of nutrients by the consumer". (Harris and Loesecke, page 174.)

Milk is heated in pasteurizing, drying, powdering, and instantizing. As a result, it suffers almost total enzyme destruction. What is the effect on protein utilization? Let's refer again to Harris and Loesecke. In reference to some studies on the effects of heat on cereal grains they said:

"This study makes it clear that lysine may become unavailable to an animal because of incomplete enzymatic digestion and/or actual destruction. *The former can occur under conditions of relatively mild heat treatment which does not necessarily cause a destruction of lysine* (emphasis) — Since lysine is the limiting amino acid of cereal proteins, the vulnerability of lysine to heat leads to a serious impairment in the nutritive quality of the protein". (ibid. p. 232.) This would also apply to milk!

Summary

To summarize the foregoing:

1. Lysine can be *destroyed* by heat. This destruction occurs to a small extent in pasteurizing, drying, and powdering of milk, and to an unknown extent in cooking bread and cereals.

2. *Destruction* of amino acids is not the only way they become unavailable to humans.

3. Milk protein *availability* to the body can be seriously impaired by mild heat when sugars in the milk combine with the lysine in such a way as to prevent its digestion and metabolism. This happens when milk is pasteurized, dried and instantized. This is true, even though the amino acid profile looks just fine and the chemical tests show no lysine destruction due to heat.

4. The destruction of milk enzymes in pasteurization reduces the availability of lysine, and this problem is compounded in drying and instantizing, *even at low temperatures.*

5. As lysine is a "limiting amino acid", **wheat and powdered milk, singly or in combination, cannot meet your protein needs,** except possibly if eaten in impractically massive amounts.

Protein Efficiency Ratio

In the final analysis, the value of a protein is determined by its P.E.R. or Protein Efficiency Ratio. This is determined by rat studies. Immature rats are fed the protein food to be tested as their only protein source. The growth promoting value of the protein is measured by weight gain. If there is no growth, the food has a P.E.R. of 1. If they double in weight, the P.E.R. is 2. If they lose weight, it would have a P.E.R. of less than 1, such as .6 or .8.

Internal Cannibalism

Why would the rats lose weight, being given "adequate" quantities of food? Simply this. Remember, the body cannot manufacture muscle tissue, hormones, connective tissue, bone protein, or other protein tissues, unless *all* the essential amino acids are present at the same time, in the right percentages, *in available form.* A low P.E.R. protein is either (a) missing an essential amino acid, (b) has one present in too small a percentage, or (c) has one or more amino acids unavailable to the body, for reasons already discussed in this chapter. Your body realizes you will die quickly unless you continually manufacture hormones (the body's regulators and long distance chemical communication system), enzymes (for digestion and all chemical reactions in the cell, without which life is impossible), and digestive acids (without which you would starve to death).

So the body begins to break down its least vital protein tissues to get the necessary amino acids to complete the amino acid profile for these functions.

The first losses are from connective tissue (collagen), which is literally the glue that holds you together. (When a horse goes to the glue factory, he is boiled down for his collagen). This is drawn first from bones, which are 40% to 60% collagen, and from support tissues under the skin. Muscle tissues goes next and finally, vital organs and nerve tissue.

So the rats lose weight steadily, sicken, and eventually die, if the deficiency continues. The lower the P.E.R., the sooner the death.

The Effect on People

The same thing can happen to humans. This is much like a family that has too little income, and has to liquidate its assets, in order to buy necessities. The importance of high P.E.R. proteins cannot be over-stated. They mean life or death, sickness or health.

What are some of the effects of a low P.E.R. diet on humans?

Children pay the highest price. Growth can stop completely as we have seen in famines in Africa and India. *And it can never be made up.*

Bones can become brittle and distorted in shape as they lose their collagen (protein) structures. Bones are 40% to 60% protein.

Allergies can develop, as the body becomes unable to digest foods properly, due to a lack of the necessary enzymes. Enzymes are made of protein.

Brain tissue stops developing, *and this can never be made up.* Brain tissue is made of protein.

The blood sugar control mechanisms become deranged, and either diabetes or hypoglycemia (low blood sugar) can develop, and along with this, emotional and mental disturbances. This is because the hormones that regulate blood sugar are made of protein.

Resistance to infection drops, as antibodies and white blood cells are made of protein.

Energy sags as the body "banks its furnaces", and concentrates on making only the most vital protein tissues as a self-preservation mechanism.

Older people begin to age rapidly and lose weight as they are unable to digest their food. Digestive acids are made of protein.

How Much Protein?

The government, in the Federal Register, says an adult needs 45 grams of protein, "if the P.E.R. is equal to or greater than that of casein", the major protein fraction from milk. Casein's P.E.R. is 2.5, about the same as most meats, fish and fowl. If you are eating a lower P.E.R. protein, you need correspondingly more. You could require as much as 130 grams of a complete but low P.E.R. protein, and *no* amount of an incomplete protein will be adequate.

It is my opinion, that you should store protein over and above your body's minimum requirements, because of the versatility of protein in the body. **The body can convert excess protein into sugar to stabilize the blood sugar levels and provide energy, whereas carbohydrates and fats can be used only to be burned as energy. (carbohydrates burn fast — like kindling and fats burn slow and hot — like coal). Protein can be used for energy *and* growth, *and* repair factors, *and* a host of vital functions.** Dietary carbohydrates are *not* essential to health, if adequate protein is supplied. The Eskimo had little or no carbohydrates in his diet, and yet he had few health problems until he adopted the white man's high carbohydrate diet. The body will make its own decisions as to how much carbohydrate or protein it will use at any given time — if adequate protein is provided. It will use the protein either way — as needed.

Most authorities agree that stress increases protein requirements. Stress could be the result of inadequate diet, fear, worries, injury, illness, surgery, medications, air pollution, and a lot of other problems. I think we can agree that the coming troubles will be a time of great stress.

It's my opinion we should aim for 60 to 90 grams of protein a day (high P.E.R., of course). But where do we get it in a famine?

No Room for Error

When the famine hits us, the first foods to become unavailable will be the high quality proteins. They don't store well. Meat, fish, eggs, fowl and dairy products won't keep, and our present fast, efficient distribution system will disappear. Unless you have a cow or goats, and some chickens (and are equipped to defend them) and have laid in a year's supply of feed for them, you will be entirely dependent on what you have stored. Let's examine some of the alternatives, and their pluses and minuses.

1. **Fresh or frozen meats, fish, and eggs.**

Obviously out because of their vulnerability, and short shelf life.

2. **Canned meats, fish and eggs.**

A possibility, but has some disadvantages. First, they are often 2 to 3 times more expensive than their fresh counterparts. That could be financially out of reach, unless you're rich.

The shelf life of some canned meats is poor, and Harris and Loesecke state, in regards to them,

"... the product should be handled and treated as a perishable product, with refrigeration recommended both before and after opening the sealed container". (Nutritional Evaluation of Food Processing — p. 268).

Canned goods also show a steady loss of nutrients over relatively short periods of storage, and are bulky and difficult to store.

3. **Wheat and Powdered Milk.**

Wheat and dry milk belong in your storage program. I have over a ton stored in my program.

Wheat

Wheat is indispensible because of its many virtues.

It can store almost forever. Some was found in King Tut's tomb, and it could still germinate. In fact, King Tut's wheat is one of of the ancestors of the new hybrid grains that have created the "Green revolution".

It supplies necessary bulk, calories and some high quality carbohydrate in the form of a highly digestible starch.

It supplies liquid fats (oils) of high quality.

It is a fine source of vitamins and minerals.

It contributes some protein.

It does have some drawbacks, however:

It is a low P.E.R. protein (.8)

More people are allergic to wheat than any other food, except possibly milk.

It contains phytic acid, a phosphorous compound which inhibits your utilization of calcium, and thus increases your calcium requirements substantially

But, all in all, because of its value, and its storability, it's indispensible in a storage program.

Dry Milk

This also belongs in your program, for several reasons:

It stores well, if properly prepared. Not as well as wheat, but satisfactorily.

It provides some minerals and vitamins, including calcium.

It also has drawbacks, some of which we have previously outlined.

It is not the equivalent of raw milk. If you think it is, you will make mistaken nutritional judgements.

It is usually made from Grade B milk. That is why it's so cheap. Grade B milk has over 10 times the bacteria count of Grade A milk. Pasteurization kills the bacteria, *but does not remove them.* Some researchers have raised questions about the effect of these dead "bugs" in the body. Some think they may cause nausea, vomiting and diarrhea in some susceptible children.

It seems more likely to cause allergic reactions, than other forms of milk. In my work with obese people, I have found that many people who are allergic to powdered milk, or even pasteurized, can often tolerate raw milk, (when they can get it). I believe it is due to the enzyme destruction we discussed earlier in this chapter, caused by pasteurizing. A good protein supplement can supply the missing enzymes, and you might want to store some natural enzyme capsules.

But most of all, it lacks *available* lysine and has a low P.E.R. But, all in all, it is definitely worth storing.

Hunting and Fishing.

This can make an obvious protein contribution, if you live in the right location and have the necessary skills and equipment. You will have problems with storage, but these foods can really help.

Combining Vegetable Proteins.

It is possible to combine different vegetable products with high protein content and complementary amino acid profiles to make complete proteins of good value. The excellent book, *"Diet for a Small Planet"* by Frances Moore Lappe' contains a lot of good material on this subject. The enthusiasm of its author notwithstanding, there are some drawbacks!

The protein percentages of beans, grains, nuts, etc., the foods usually recommended, are pretty low, ranging from 9% to 30%. The rest is mostly carbohydrate — 60% to 80%. As stress shifts your dietary requirements away from carbohydrate toward protein, you will be out of balance. If you eat enough of these foods to meet your protein requirements under stress conditions, you will consume too much carbohydrate. If you can't burn it all for energy, you will store it as fat. You can't use it for anything else, as it has no body building value. It is only useful for energy. In my opinion, you are out of balance, *if you depend on vegetable proteins as your primary protein source.* But I would certainly make these foods part of my program and use them.

Protein Concentrates.

There is a thriving, growing market for protein concentrates in powder form in cans. These are available in health food stores, drug stores, supermarkets, and through direct distributors in your neighborhood. In my opinion, this is by far the best basic solution for your program. You can mix these in reconstituted powdered milk, and actually convert the milk back into the life-giving food you thought it was before you read this chapter. In fact, one 8 oz. serving of dry milk with one ounce of a good protein concentrate with a high P.E.R. can give more value than 6 glasses of raw milk, or many more glasses of dry milk alone. That serving, taken with whole wheat bread or cereal, can supply the missing lysine and enzymes, (if it is extra rich in lysine and contains enzymes) and convert the bread and cereal, into high P.E.R. proteins. This achieves what the sincere myth-makers thought they were achieving with powdered milk alone. The problem is how do you tell a good concentrate from a poor one. There is a lot of humbuggery in the field. Recently, the distributors of one of the largest selling brands conducted some P.E.R. studies with rats, using their product, and the rats began to die.

In determining quality, you must consider shelf life,

P.E.R., ingredient ratio, amino acid profile, protein sources used, temperature used in the processing, quantity and quality of sweeteners used, digestibility, (due to quantity and quality of enzymes used) percentage of protein in the can, mixability; and, last but far from least, palatability or taste.

Suffice it to say here, it's almost impossible for the layman to tell the difference. In Chapter XIV, when I discuss protein concentrates, I won't name my favorite brand, because I sell it, but I'll tell you how to tell a good one from a bad one.

CHAPTER IX

T.V.P. — The Great Imposter

Extravagant claims are being made for soybeans for storage programs, and especially for T.V.P. — Textured Vegetable Proteins. These are meat analogs — processed soya protein which has been spun into fibers, or extruded at high heat under great pressure, to be made into a food product of the same texture as meat. It is flavored and shaped to look and taste like beef, ham, pork, bacon, etc. Some of it, in my opinion, borders on being tasty.

T.V.P. has found its way into commercial storage programs, because it dehydrates well, and when canned, it keeps almost indefinitely.

Is it the answer to the protein problem? Let's look at its strengths and weaknesses.

T.V.P. — The Good Points

1. It can be tasty — but not as good as meat.
2. It stores well. Meat does not.
3. It has some nutrients inherent in the soybean

from which it is made. For example, a fairly good amino acid profile, lecithin, and some of the B complex.

4. It is versatile when used as an extender of meat.
5. It is cheaper than meat.

The Other Side of the Coin

Although T.V.P. belongs in your program, it has some serious drawbacks you should be aware of.

1. **Deceptive.** Because it looks, and feels, and tastes like meat, you might erroneously conclude it is as nourishing as meat. This error could cause you to assume you are better nourished than you really are.

2. **Poor Amino Acid Availability.** Soybeans are low in methionine, one of the essential amino acids. But the real problem is tryptophan, (pronounced trip' — toe — fain), one of the "limiting" amino acids. When the product is extruded, the resulting heat and pressure bring about an enzymatic change, converting an enzyme into an "anti-trypsin inhibitor". Trypsin is the enzyme your body needs to break down tryptophan. The inhibitor makes that impossible.

This reduces the "N.S.I." — Nitrogen Solubility Index. This is an indicator of the body's capacity to use the protein. When soy protein is heated in processing, the N.S.I. drops from 90% or more, down to about 15%. The Department of Agriculture allows T.V.P. to be used in school lunches as a meat extender, but no more than 30%, because of the mediocre amino acid profile. When rehydrated, T.V.P. is about 17% protein, about the same as meat, although, of course, it has a lower P.E.R.

3. **P.E.R. Unknown.** All the published P.E.R. studies are with the uncooked product. They range from "low" (1.2) up to, "not bad" (2.1). But what happens to the P.E.R. when it is cooked? I haven't been able to find any rat studies on the cooked product. Based on what heat does to the Soya Nitrogen Solubility Index, the P.E.R. is undoubtedly drastically reduced.

4. **Chemical Additives.** Whenever you have a man-made highly processed manufactured food, you find synthetic flavor enhancers, antioxidents, colorings, and preservatives. Most of these are on a list, kept by the F.D.A., known as the GRAS list (Generally Recognized As Safe). These are food additives that were in common use by processors *prior to* the laws regulating additives. The F.D.A. did not have the money or the staff to test them all. Such tests can take years. So the industry simply submitted a list, which the F.D.A. accepted. Almost every year one or more of these substances is found to cause cancer, or other dangerous conditions, and is removed from the list. This usually happens only after months of denials from the F.D.A., and the industry, and after the evidence is overwhelming.

Let's look at the ingredient list of some pork-flavored T.V.P. from a large manufacturer. This is a typical formula. Remember — the ingredients are listed in *descending* order.

"Soy flour, salt, hydrolyzed vegetable protein, whey solids, flavoring, monosodium glutamate, spice, hydrogenated vegetable oil, disodium inosinate, disodium guanylate, and U.S. Certified color."

Doesn't that sound tasty? Let's look at some of the ingredients:

Salt (Sodium): Present in large amounts. It's the 2nd ingredient listed. In addition, sodium is present in the monosodium-glutamate, disodium inosinate, and the disodium guanylate. Sodium should be limited by persons with hypertension (high blood pressure), heart disease, and water retention problems. T.V.P. is loaded with it.

Whey Solids: See Chapter VIII and refresh your memory on the value of heated whey products.

Monosodium Glutamate: (MSG) This is the principle ingredient in such flavor enhancers as Accent. It was universally used in commercially prepared baby foods (so *mother* will think it tastes good) — until studies determined beyond question that it causes brain damage in young animals. It is now illegal to use it in baby foods, as a result of the findings.

M.S.G. is used in most T.V.P.! It has been identified as the cause of the "Chinese Restaurant Syndrome" where people who have had a Chinese dinner suffer from severe migraine-like headaches a few hours later.

Foods treated with large quantities of M.S.G. should be taken sparingly, and should not be fed to infants and toddlers.

Hydrogenated Vegetable Oil. Liquid fats (vegetable oils) are highly unsaturated, with the exception of coconut oil. Polyunsaturated oils are generally thought by cardiologists and nutritionists to lower cholesterol and triglyceride (fat) levels in the blood. When a food processor wishes to harden the oil to get a different consistency (such as making margarine out of corn or safflower oil), or to prolong its shelf life, he "hydrogenates" it. It is heated under pressure and hydrogen is bubbled through it in the presence of a metal catalyst (nickel or platinum). The hydrogen atoms combine with the carbon atoms and the product becomes highly saturated, and hardens.

Dr. Bicknell describes it as follows:

> "The abnormal fatty acids produced by "hardening" (hydrogenation) are the real worry. The atoms of the molecule of an essential fatty acid (EFA.) are arranged in space in a particular manner . . . but hardening may produce a different spatial arrangement, so that a completely abnormal . . . essential fatty acid is produced. An analogy is ordinary handwriting and mirror handwriting: both are identical but spatially different, so that at best reading the latter is difficult and at worst serious mistakes are made. The same mistakes are made by the body when presented . . . (with the abnormal EFA.) Not only does it fail to benefit by them, but it is deluded by their similarity to normal EFA and so attempts to use them. It starts incorporating them in biochemical reactions and then finds they are the wrong shape: but the reaction has gone too far to jettison them and begin again with normal EFA, so they are not only useless but actually prevent the use of normal EFA. They are

> in fact *anti*-EFA. They accentuate in man and animals a deficiency of EFA. An analogy is jamming the wrong key in a lock: not only is the lock not turned but the right key also is rendered valueless."

Franklin Bicknell, M.D. *Chemicals in Food and Farm Produce: Their Harmful Effects.* (London: Faber and Faber 1960 — pp. 69-70.)

These super-saturated fats may be a factor in heart disease. Ironically, the processors of T.V.P. tout its low fat content and lack of cholesterol, implying it helps to prevent heart disease. The experts are not agreed on that, but I believe it is harmful, and is a far greater health danger than natural saturated fats.

U.S. Certified Colorings: You have been eating these all your life, but no one knows what their *cumulative* effect is. Ninety percent of all dyes used are synthetic. Of the 82 food dyes used in 22 countries, only one is permitted in all of them. Several coal tar and other chemical dyes have been "de-certified", as they have been shown to cause cancer.

Red Dye #1 was used widely for years, and was officially "safe". Finally rat studies were done. 250 rats were fed foods containing varying amounts. 116 died and others suffered liver damage and malignant tumors. It has been de-certified. Perhaps too late for some!

Flavorings. They are all synthetic, in the same category as colorings, in my opinion.

A Cause of Allergies

Dr. Benjamin F. Fiengold, Chief Emeritus of the Department of Allergy at the Kaiser Foundation Hospitals, has traced about 70% of all childhood allergies to chemical additives. He found that children, who were thought to be allergic to certain foods, were found to be allergic instead to the colorings, flavorings, stabilizers and preservatives, but the prime factors were the colorings. They caused hyperactivity and behavior problems.

You Can't Avoid It

Food additives appear to be unavoidable. If you live on a farm, and eat nothing but fresh food, you might avoid them. But storage foods are another matter. Even if all the additives were safe *individually,* no one knows what their cumulative effect might be. Chemical compounds change their characteristics when combined with other compounds, or sometimes spontaneously after a time lapse. The average American eats 3 to 7 *pounds* of these dubious, inadequately tested compounds each year, some of which accumulate in body fat, bones, or vital organs, with unknown long-term cumulative effects. Allergy may be only the tip of the iceberg. I'm not fanatic enough to say a little bit will kill you. I also recognize it may be unavoidable in a storage program, as some of these additives preserve and stabilize foods, or make them palatable. There are two steps I can suggest, however.

1. Limit your intake of T.V.P. and foods containing

additives. Concentrate on natural grains, and dried fruits and vegetables, processed as little as possible. Check your dehydrated foods for additives and make the processor tell you which ones have them, and which ones don't. Make as few compromises as possible. **During normal times you can choose what you will or will not buy, to eliminate additives. But, when the famine comes, you're stuck with what you stored. Choose wisely.**

2. Block the effects of these toxic substances by good nutrition. Vitamin C, for example, is believed by some respectable authorities to combine with toxins and neutralize them. Vitamin E is thought to have similar effects. The F.D.A. is now considering regulations *requiring* processors of meat products using sodium nitrate and sodium nitrite to add Vitamin C to their products. This is due to the fact that nitrate and nitrite form "Nitrosamines" in the stomach. These are among the most potent carcinogens (cancer causing agents) known to man, and are routinely used to *cause* cancer in laboratory rats. Vitamin C, if in the stomach *at the same time,* blocks the conversion of nitrates and nitrites into nitrosamines. These poisons are found in weiners, lunch meat, ham, bacon, all canned or process meats — and often T.V.P.

Should you Store T.V.P.?

On balance, I say yes. If you know what it is — and what it isn't, it can be useful. It provides useful amino acids. It adds variety, calories, bulk and taste. Take it in the same meal with your protein concentrates, and you obtain complete protein value. Take Vitamin C with it (and perhaps Vitamin E) and you may block its potential harmful effects. Use it sparingly, and don't feed it to infants and toddlers.

In summary, it is not the miracle food you might have thought. Despite man's pride, he has still not been able to duplicate nature. I am convinced that the more man tries to make food, the more he processes and invents, the poorer the food is.

Part III
The Answers – A Consumer's Guide

In this section we will teach you the basic principles of nutrition as they relate to food storage. We will show you how to meet your requirements and then some. You will be able to evaluate foods realistically so you can look at commercial storage programs, and do-it-yourself programs, and do the right thing for your family.

We will not cover the same ground covered by other books anymore than is necessary for continuity, but will refer you to the appropriate books.

Consider this a "Consumers' Guide" to commercial food storage programs, so you can demand what's best for your family — so *you* can make the nutritional decisions that could save your life, and not leave that to someone else's judgment.

CHAPTER X

The Target

Think of your food storage program as though it were a target. The most points are in the bullseye, and you receive lesser points as you move to the outside.

In this section we will discuss the ideal food storage program, arranged on a target as follows:

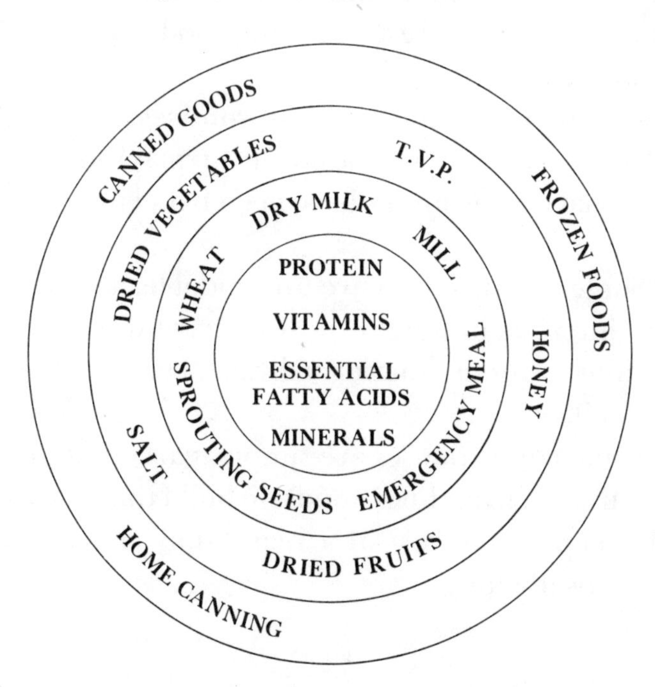

Several factors have dictated the arrangement and relative values:

1. **Nutrition.** During a food crisis, especially a prolonged one, every ounce of food must count to the highest possible degree. Some foods count more than others.

2.**Potential Scarcity.** The bullseye items will be those things that are most likely to disappear in a real food crunch, and are the most essential to life.

3. **Balance.** I have had frank "let-your-hair-down" talks with executives of food storage companies. They all concede that their largest, most stubborn problem was to get true, balanced nutrition in their total program — and in each meal — and in palatable form so children will eat it. In all modern famines, children have died in the presence of food that might have saved them, but if it was strange, or they didn't like it, they wouldn't eat it. Many of the good companies have been forced to make compromises in the interest of having food people will like, buy, and eat.

4. **Other Nutritional Compromises.** Although the food salesman may not admit it (or may not know it), nutritional compromises have been made in every program.

Some compromises are unavoidable, and are made in the interests of long term storage, and usually mean omissions of foods you normally eat, because they don't store well.

Some compromises are simply marketing decisions — the use of cheap filler-foods, to build the total calories while keeping the cost of a year "unit" attractively but unrealistically low.

Some compromises are simply from ignorance, as some food storage companies aren't nutritionally well-educated, but are sincerely ignorant.

These compromises result in the following problems:

a. **Poor quality proteins.** Good animal proteins don't store well and are omitted.

b. **Processing losses.** Vitamins, minerals, enzymes, and amino acids are damaged or lost. Sometimes the extent of those losses is known to be substantial. In some cases their extent is unknown because insufficient study has been done.

c. **Storage losses.** These may have occurred *before* the sales company canned the food.

d. **Too much carbohydrate,** — in relation to Protein and fats.

Target — Key to Health

This program is designed to solve these problems and compensate for the compromises. I will describe it as I planned it for my family. I will show you the strengths and weaknesses of each ring on the target. Our overriding concern will be good nutrition. When the famine comes you will need a strong body and an alert mind. You must stay free from illness. You must meet the demands of stress. Every ounce of food must count, because there is no going back.

The major theme running through this section is: **If we can be sure your requirements for essential nutrients have been met from your bullseye, then the**

necessary compromises can be accepted! Then the outer rings of your target become less crucial, and can be determined by budget and preference.

Let's begin with the outer ring.

CHAPTER XI

The Short Term Solution: Canned and Frozen Foods

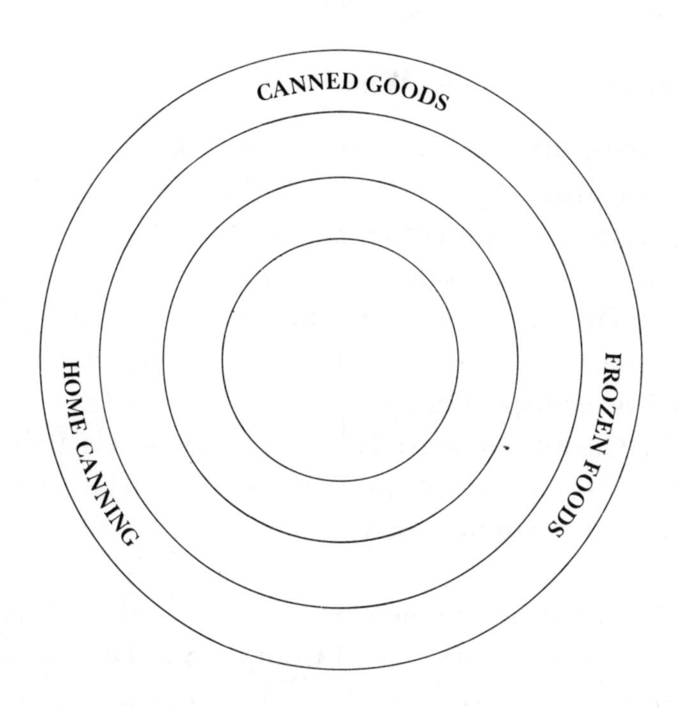

We predicted in Chapter VI that there would be some short term problems — temporary shortages caused by strikes, politics or natural calamities disrupting distribution. For that reason we might have some short term storage foods on hand.

Frozen Foods

Stock your freezer, and rotate the foods (use and systematically replace). If you store a lot of meat, buy or make a small *smoker unit.* If the power goes out for awhile, you need to have some way of extending the life of the food. If it thaws, *don't refreeze it! Smoke it.* This gives you three or four more months of shelf life. This is *not* part of your *long term* storage program.

Canned Goods — (Wet Pack)

I have many friends who have based their storage program around canned goods. This is *not* part of your long term program either. Canned goods have several serious defects for long term storage.

1. **They are bulky and heavy.** They take up far more space than dried foods. They are not easily concealed or transported.

2. **Costly.** Compared to dehydrated foods, they are very expensive. You seem to get more for your money, because of the bulk, but you are buying water at food prices.

3. **Nutritionally poor.** High heats used in canning, damage the vitamin C, the B Complex, and enzymes, to say nothing of protein. They lose nutritional value rapidly, and after 6 months to a year, their value is dubious at best.

4. **Sugar loaded.** Canners just can't resist the temptation to add sugar to everything. It has a mild preservative effect and caters to the national sweet tooth, but adds nothing but empty calories and cavities. During a famine

or social breakdown, you need cavities like you need a hole in the head.

Still, for the short term, you could store some canned goods. Here are some suggestions:

1. **Store large cans.** #10 if possible. But check price per pound to be sure it is the best buy. It may not be.

2. **Store canned tuna.** It is your best canned protein buy. Its amino acid content has been damaged somewhat by heat, and I wouldn't trust it beyond 6 months, but as a rotation item for short term, it's a good buy. Buy the oil-pack variety.

3. **Date the cans** and use them within 6 months.

4. **Stick with simple basics.** Vegetables, beans, fruits (in water or *light* syrup), tuna, etc. Ignore the combination foods such as stews, spaghetti, etc. Don't pay for flour and pasta at canned food prices. You can make your own combinations.

5. **Rotate and replace regularly.** *Remember, this is not your long-term storage program. This is for temporary, short term shortages, and could be dispensed with entirely.* But go ahead, if you'd like.

CHAPTER XII

Bulk, Variety and Calories

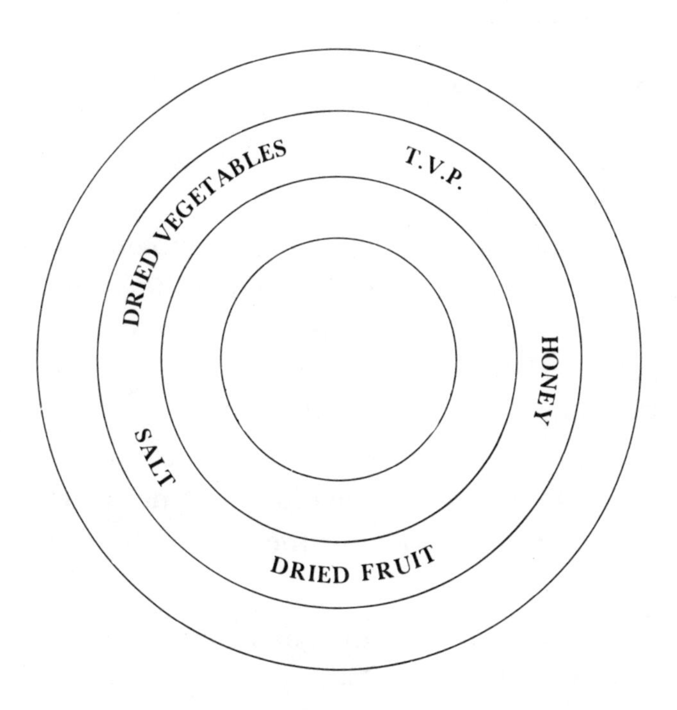

In this ring of our target we have encompassed most of the food sold by the commercial storage companies. These programs are touted as being "complete" and nutritionally balanced. They are not, in my opinion. They are necessary and useful, but fall far short of completeness.

Let's examine these items, one by one.

Perhaps the greatest single boon to food storage programs since the invention of wheat, are the dehydrated fruits and vegetables. They save weight, and space, and when properly prepared for storage, will keep almost indefinitely. The taste sometimes can hardly be distinguished from fresh or frozen foods, and they are relatively cheap. They provide a good amount of fiber and roughage.

The Necessary Compromises

Some critical compromises have been made in the interest of long term storage.

1. **Processing.** All the storage companies buy from a handful of major processors. Then they can it themselves. Regardless of what they say, despite their claims, no one knows the actual nutritional value of the food by the time you get it on your shelf.

A technical bulletin issued by California Vegetable Concentrates (C.V.C.), a Division of General Foods that makes dehydrated foods for the storage food industry, says:

> "There is no truly reliable, representative nutritional information pertaining to commercially processed dehydrated vegetables. What work has been done on processed vegetables has been fragmentary, difficult to correlate for many reasons and of only indicative value in determining food values.
>
> . . . "Values shown for dehydrated vegetables have been calculated based on concentration ratios *with no assumed processing losses.*"

This means that nutritional tables for dried foods

are an approximation at best.

Nutrient values are lost in processing to an undetermined degree. It can be assumed that such losses are no greater than those from other processes (canning, freezing, etc.), but are substantial.

Often, however, judgements are made as to the nutritional value of storage programs *based on raw, unprocessed food values.* These are not the same, so you will have to make your nutritional judgements based on *estimated* losses from processing.

Nutrients are lost in blanching *prior to drying.* Much of the self-serving literature from the industry concentrates only on the losses from drying, which are relatively minor.

2. **Additives.** All processors use additives to some degree. This affects the nutritional content adversely. Sodium sulfite and sodium bisulfite are often used in dehydrated vegetables. This tends to preserve the carotene (the vegetable source of Vitamin A) but destroys Thiamine (B-1) and to a lesser extent Riboflavin, Niacin, and Panthothenic Acid, other members of the B complex. Vitamin C is also lost in processing and drying.

Vitamin Losses from Sulfites

Vitamin	Percentage of Loss
Thiamine	10% to 40%
Riboflavin	0% to 15%
Niacin	0% to 12%
Pantothenic Acid	0% to 28%
Vitamin C	Average 50%

(C.V.C. Technical Bulletin)

The B vitamins and Vitamin C are needed in larger, not smaller, amounts in times of stress. And famine is a time of stress!

The effect of sulfite on the B vitamins is so great that it should not be used in processing foods known to be a good source of B vitamins. For this reason U.S.D.A. regulations do not allow using ingredients containing sulphite in excess of 200 P.P.M. (Parts Per Million) in meat products.

Nutrient Retention Under Storage Conditions

For information, let's turn again to the C.V.C. Technical Bulletin:

> "*We know of no data indicating retention of nutritional values after prolonged storage.* CVC dehydrated vegetables do retain good *color* and *flavor* for periods in excess of one year and in several instances for considerably longer periods when held at 70 degrees Fahrenheit or below. At zero degrees Fahrenheit, storage life appears to be unlimited".

3. **Selection.** Many foods are omitted because they don't dry well, or would be too expensive, or are too fatty (which means rapid rancidity). This means that many foods which presently keep you reasonably well-nourished won't be there, and the substitutes aren't as valuable as what they have replaced. I'm referring to

fresh meat, eggs, fish, dairy products which presently provide most of your protein, and a substantial amount of vitamins A and B. The major protein substitutes (beans, rice, etc.) are both lower protein percentage, and much lower protein quality, even when combined.

High Carbohydrates

Relying on mostly vegetable proteins for your amino acids means a diet higher in carbohydrates (starches and sugars) than is sensible for a survival, anti-stress program.

A "Small Planet" Revisted

Many storage programs have been influenced by the "complementary protein" concepts of Frances Moore Lappe, in her book "Diet For a Small Planet". You can combine vegetable proteins in such a way as to increase their value. For instance, if you combine wheat (low in lysine) with rice (high in lysine), you improve the value of both proteins.

Don't overestimate the value of this process, however, to the extent of over-dependence on vegetable proteins. If you do, you will be deficient in B-12 and will be consuming from 4 to 5 times as much carbohydrate as protein. That is a bad ratio for a stress diet. Don't eat these starchy foods to excess.

How Much Should I Store?

Store a *year's* supply of basics. We have a one year

crop cycle is this country. By basics, I mean avoiding cheap fillers. Many programs include large amounts of gelatin (a lousy quality protein, missing several essential amino acids), macaroni, white flour, etc. This builds calories cheaply, but has very little other value. **Remember, every ounce must count to the limit.**

Here is a list of dried storage foods I recommend and the approximate amounts per adult per year:

Fruit (Dry weight)	**Vegetables (Dry weight)**	**Beans**
Apple slices 4-5 lbs.	Green peas 8-10 lbs.	100 lbs
Apricot slices 4-5 lbs.	Carrots 5-6 lbs.	
Fruit Blend 8-10 lbs.	Stew mix 5-6 lbs.	
Prunes (whole-pitted) 8-10 lbs.	Tomato crystals 8-10 lbs.	
	Potatoes 15-20 lbs.	

Peanut Butter (Dry weight)	**Cheese (Dried)**
8-10 lbs.	8-10 lbs

Should I Store Dehydrates?

A resounding "Yes", but observe some precautions:

1. **Buy from reputable companies.** But be careful! Some of the biggest names are shaky financially, due to poor management and under-capitalization, and have a poor record on deliveries.

2. **Don't buy the cheapest!** It is possible to take seconds, old crop which have been stored uncanned and unprepared for storage by the prime processor before it got to the storage company which cans it and sells it to you. This enables the sales company to sell cheap and still make good money. The loser is the consumer, due to the lower nutritional value, taste and flavor.

3. **Buy nitrogen-pack in #2½ cans,** not institutional size #10 cans. Be sure there is no more than 3% residual oxygen in the can. This extends shelf life almost indefinitely, and sharply reduces storage nutritional losses. With small cans you are not going to have losses due to oxidation after they are opened, as the smaller amounts will will be used up quickly. A #10 can of dried apples makes 14 lbs. of apples! Nutritional losses are significant by the 3rd day after opening, and up to 75% after the 6th day. Nitrogen-pack and small cans cost more, but it's a lot cheaper than losing your food supply to spoilage, or becoming ill from inadequate nutrition.

4. **Store water.** It takes a lot of water to reconstitute dehydrates. Have an emergency supply of 10 gallons per family member **minimum.** Also buy an inexpensive water purifier.

Incidently, the greatest water storage idea I ever heard of is the water-bed — 175 gal. for a King Size, 135 Gal. for a Queen Size, down to 90 gal. for a twin. With a small water purifier, you're all set.

5. **Check your program to be sure you have bought enough.** As we have said before, many commercial programs base their one year food requirements on unrealistically small amounts of food, in the interest of claiming a low price for a "unit" of food. In fact, you should store about 20% more than you feel you need for your family, plus some for your relatives, plus extra for barter as a medium of exchange.

6. Recognize that the principal value of your dehydrated foods is to provide bulk, variety, taste, and extra calories. The way we have structured your target,

the nutritional deficits will be met from your bullseye. This makes other food selections much less critical, giving you a lot more flexibility and freedom of choice. The nutrients in the dried foods become a bonus.

T.V.P.

In Chapter IX we discussed the positive and negative aspects of T.V.P. I'd like to give you a few hints about its use, and reiterate some cautions:

1. Use it sparingly. Use it in soups and stews, and as a meat extender, not as a one-for-one meat substitute.
2. Keep it from infants and toddlers, because of the monosodium glutamate, as explained in Chapter IX.
3. Store about 6-8 lbs. (dry weight) per person.

Honey

Honey belongs in your storage program, but I don't consider honey one of the essentials. That's why it's in an outer ring on your target. In my opinion, it should be used as a *condiment* — not a food. It provides almost pure carbohydrates in the form of sugars. This is "good news" and "bad news". The bad news first.

1. Sugar is not an essential human nutrient. Your body can make sugar from protein and fats.
2. It is so rapidly absorbed that it hits you all at once! If you have a need for immediate explosive effort, that's good. If you are not extremely active physically, that's bad. It either burns fast like paper in a fire, or is stored as fat if it is not burned up immediately by activity. I would much rather see you get most of your carbohy-

drate in the form of more slowly absorbed starches, from wheat and dried fruits and vegetables.

3. Starches are converted to blood sugar anyway, so they will do the energy job as well as sugars, whether from honey or sucrose (table sugar). Just a bit slower.

Now the good news!

1. Honey is better for you than table sugar.

2. It has small amounts of minerals and vitamins, if you get the unfiltered, unprocessed type. Sometimes (but not always) this is darker, stronger in taste, and tends to crystallize easier, but it's better for you.

3. Honey is sweeter to taste than table sugar, so you tend to eat less to get the same sweetening effect.

4. It is a healthful substitute for sugar in baking such things as whole wheat bread, and because it is sweeter, you use less.

5. Honey is richer in fructose, which makes it a bit safer for the diabetic or the hypoglycemic. It can provide some calories to meet your total caloric requirements. Remember, treat honey as a healthful condiment, not as a food. You need 50 to 100#.

"A Calorie Is A Calorie, Is A Calorie —"

You have daily caloric requirements. If you take in less than your caloric requirements, you will tend to lose weight. If you have extra fat to lose, that's O.K. If you don't have extra fat, you will lose vital tissue and muscle if you don't meet your caloric requirements.

Average Calories Required Daily

Adult Male	2500-3500
Adult Female	2200-2700
Teen-Agers	2500-3000

It is in the number of calories stored that most commercial food storage companies fall short. It takes a lot of research to find out the true calorie count of a storage program. In the interest of reducing the cost of a one year "unit", the sheer quantity of food may have been reduced to unrealistically low levels by the sales companies.

Remember the following:

A gram of protein has 4.2 calories.

A gram of carbohydrate has 4.2 calories.

A gram of fat has 9.2 calories.

If you store dehydrated fruits and vegetables, wheat and powdered milk, you will have all the carbohydrate you need, and then some. In my opinion, over 65% of your total calories should come from protein and fats.

Calories From Fats.

Because of its high caloric count (9.2 per gram), fats can give you the most calorie value for the least money, in the smallest space.

With the current concern about fats and heart disease, it would be best to put that back in perspective.

If you get about 60% of your fats from polyunsaturated oils, your body can handle the saturated variety just fine. You should store some oils, such as corn oil, peanut oil or safflower oil in *dark* bottles, tightly sealed. Store peanuts, peanut butter, cashews, sunflower seeds, sesame seeds, canned or hermetically sealed in bottles. They are rich in oils, and help build the calorie count. Oils must be protected from oxygen, or they become rancid. This is definitely a rotation item as shelf life is limited.

Watch out for hydrogenated fats. See Chapter IX for a review of why. Hydrogenation does increase storage life, but at the cost of your health. I believe these are dangerous fats. At the present I am looking for a method of long term storage for fats, or possibly nuts and seeds with good oil content, to provide calories and Essential Fatty Acids. If we are able to do so, I'll include the information in later editions.

Salt

Salt is needed in the diet, but if you store as we have recommended, you probably have enough in your diet for health. T.V.P. is rich in salt. So are some of the dried vegetables.

Your salt needs increase when you live in a hot climate and perspire a lot. Less is needed during winter. It should be limited if there is a history of obesity, heart trouble or high blood pressure.

You need it for cooking, seasoning, etc. But, like honey, it is a condiment, not a food. Five pounds per person should be sufficient.

CHAPTER XIII

The Target — Getting Closer

The First Ring out from the Bullseye is of great importance. It's getting close to the bullseye. It is designed to meet your basic needs for bulk, calories, taste, and some concentrated emergency meals.

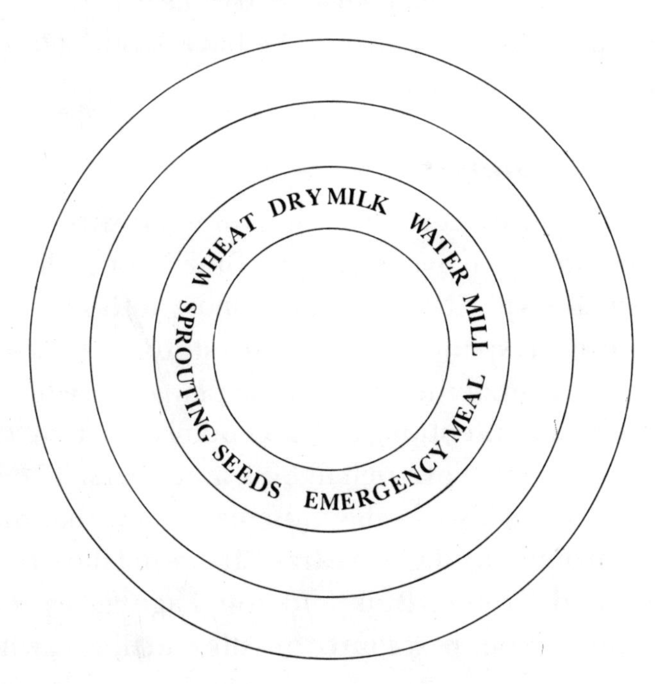

The Emergency Meal

There will be times when you need to travel away from home, or won't be able to cook for some reason. You need some kind of compact, concentrated emergency food that is a balanced meal all by itself. The Army has its K rations and its C rations.

I suggest you obtain some candy-bar-like meals that are available today, and have them on hand for short-term use. Our family uses one that is delicious, filling, and nutritionally balanced, except for adequate calories. Its shelf life is only about 6 months, but it is now being canned for longer life. Because of its low calorie count, it is not for long term use, unless you have extra fat to burn, but it is great for short-term use. We use it now when hiking, fishing, skiing, and traveling. It weighs only 2½ ounces. Ten pounds provides 64 meals! It's also a nourishing treat for children. We have about 100 meals per family member

Bulk and Calories

You require a certain amount of non-nutritive fiber to maintain an active properly functioning digestive tract. Dr. Burkitt, the world's foremost authority on intestinal cancer, spent years in Africa studying tribes who never get cancer of the colon. His explanation, which has received wide attention and acceptance, is that these tribes eat diets that are rich in bulk and fibers. The bulk stimulates peristalsis — the muscular action that moves matter through the digestive tract. It doesn't have time to putrefy and irritate. Bulk and roughage also prevent constipation. Your best source of bulk and fiber is wheat.

Wheat — The Staff of Life

1. Whole wheat provides excellent bulk and roughage from the bran layer. Properly prepared it stores forever. It is a source of some protein. (See Chapter VIII for its protein limitations). It provides easily digestible high quality carbohydrate in the form of starches. It is a rich source of the B Complex, Vitamin E, and has some Essential Fatty Acids. It is rich in Iron and other minerals. It provides much needed calories.

It has only a few disadvantages. Its protein is of poor quality, unless supplemented: It lacks lysine. Many people are allergic to it. It requires grinding and cooking, which requires some equipment and skill. And it's bulky and heavy to store or transport.

But it's essential for your program.

Others have written extensively about wheat and its uses and its preparation. I recommend *"Wheat For Man"* and *"Making the Best of Basics"* for guidance along these lines.

You need 50 to 200 lbs. per person, depending on what else you have.

Wheat Mill

In our target on page 131 we have a wheat mill. You can obtain hand grinders very inexpensively. They don't do as good a job of grinding and protecting the fragile, delicate wheat nutrients, as an electric powered stone mill. These are quite costly, but worth it, especially if they have a manual operation feature in case of no electricity. But test the manual function *with wheat in it,* to be sure you really could grind a good batch of wheat by hand without busting a gusset. The savings effected by buying whole wheat and grinding your own flour will pay for it in a year or less.

Powdered Milk

Earlier we discussed the disadvantages of powdered milk. Now let's look at its virtues.

Calcium in Milk

Milk is a fine calcium source, although some calcium is lost from dried milk in processing. That's the "Milkstone" that builds up in the pasteurizing equipment. In my opinion, the amounts of milk you would use would not provide enough calcium to meet your increased requirement caused by the wheat in your diet, but it is obviously a major contribution. Milk calcium is among the most soluble forms in the body.

Protein in Milk

Even though the lysine may be unavailable, and powdered milk, by itself or with wheat, is not a terribly important protein, it does provide some valuable amino acids. Its prime function in my program is to have something in which to mix my protein concentrate. This converts the milk into a fine, complete high potency protein. Eight ounces of milk, (reconstituted) with ½ oz. to 1 oz. of protein concentrate (if it is high in lysine) is the equivalent in protein value of 6 glasses of whole raw milk, or 15 to 20 glasses of reconstituted dry milk alone.

Lactose — Milk Sugar

Milk is rich in a complex sugar called lactose. This is more slowly absorbed than most sugars, and is handled better. Some people are allergic to milk, however, and it is usually an allergic reaction to the lactose. They are lacking in *lactase,* the enzyme required for the digestion of lactose. This can *sometimes* be overcome by taking tiny amounts of milk, (2 drops in a glass of water) and gradually building up the amount until your body produces sufficient lactase. Sometimes some natural enzyme capsules will help.

Dry milk does belong in your program, but in one of the outer rings, not the bullseye.

This is also a rotation item. Although it won't become inedible for years if properly canned, its nutritional values drop steadily, and its value is almost gone in two years.

You need 50-100 lbs. per person.

CHAPTER XIV

The Bullseye — Protein

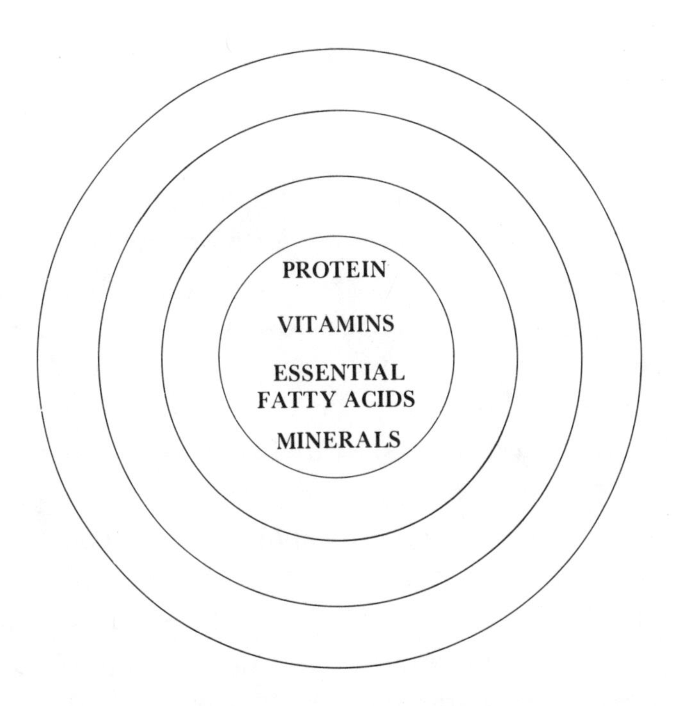

We have now arrived at the center of our program. Most storage programs stop here and assume they are complete, but as we have noted, many compromises have been made, leaving us with some serious deficiencies.

1. Poor quality protein (low P.E.R.) (especially low in tryptophan and lysine).

2. Too much carbohydrate relative to protein.

3. Vitamin C destroyed in processing.

4. B Vitamins damaged in processing.

5. Calcium deficiency caused by the high grain intake.

6. Essential fatty acids in short supply because fats don't store well.

As you can see, if we don't solve these problems, there is a serious potential for health problems.

The bullseye concept is the answer.

Protein

If we were to wring all of the water out of you and separate the rest into basic components, about 70% would be protein. Your skin, hair, muscle tissue, enzymes, hormones, digestive acids, brain, heart, lungs and over half the weight of your bones is protein. You have some protein loss every day. Your skin continuously peels off its outer layers. Your hair grows steadily. You use up enzymes, hormones, digestive fluids. All protein tissue must be continually replaced. This can only be done from protein in the diet. We have already discussed in Chapter VIII the best solution to the problem. We feel you should build around a good protein concentrate. If the concentrate is adequate, it will increase the biological value of the other proteins in the diet, including the incomplete ones, *if it is consumed at the same time, in the same meal.*

Advantages of Protein in Concentrate Form

1. **Compactness.** If the world should become as chaotic as I think it will be, our food storage must be portable and concealable.

Because it is a concentrate, you get a lot of value with only a small weight and space penalty. If I had to leave suddenly and had to choose a limited amount of bulk and weight, I'd choose my protein concentrates. Protein is super essential, and will be most difficult to obtain in a crunch.

2. **Standard Value.** You know precisely how much protein you are getting each time you use some. If you have to ration your food supply, you can do so precisely.

3. **Shelf Life.** Its shelf life compares favorably with any other storage foods.

4. **No cooking needed.** This is a major advantage. If we have no electricity or gas, then coal, charcoal, or good burning woods will need to be conserved. I've heard food storage people talk about the need to store foods like those you are accustomed to, and I've attended elegant tasting, elaborate, demonstration meals made from dehydrated foods. I'm sure that would be pleasant, under ideal conditions, and there is no question that these demonstrations sell a lot of storage food.

But, I can't believe we will have the facilities, the leisure or the fuel to prepare elegant, elaborate meals. Realistically, if we have an extended period of use of our storage foods, we will also have a breakdown of services and maybe a breakdown of order in society. (Not maybe — probably!) **We will be eating for survival, not recreation.** Nutrition comes before everything. That doesn't mean our concentrates and our food shouldn't taste good. It can and it should. Just be sure to stay with the basics.

How to Use a Protein Concentrate

It is a good food in and of itself. When one ounce is mixed with 8 ounces of reconstituted dry milk, it can be used as a whole meal. It converts the milk from a dubious food into a superior food. **A small glass of it, taken with a meal of T.V.P. and vegetable proteins can complete the amino acid profile for these foods, and thus convert them into high P.E.R. proteins. To put it another way, a meal of dehydrated foods, wheat bread and T.V.P, could be deceptively satisfying, but nutritionally incomplete. With a glass of protein concentrate it would be transformed into an exceptionally sound meal.**

It can also be added to bread, or meat loaf made from T.V.P., or poured onto wheat cereal in place of milk and sugar (delicious), converting these incomplete proteins into complete ones of high value.

The Sheep from the Goats

Here is a list of the factors that make up the ideal protein concentrate.

1. **Good Taste.** If you or your children don't like it, you won't eat it. *Don't buy without tasting!*

2. **Solubility.** Most concentrates have a "grit factor" that makes them seem as though they were mixed on a beach in a high wind. Be sure it will mix with a hand shaker or with a spoon. This is one indication as to whether or not it is soluble in the body.

3. **Percentage of Protein.** If the product is over 75% protein, the ratio is O.K., depending on what the label says is in there with it. If it is over 90% protein and tastes good, you know that is has artificial sweeteners, such as saccharine, which are *many* times sweeter than sugar, and that's not desirable in a long term storage program. The scientific data is not yet all in on the effects of long term use of saccharine. There is some evidence it may cause cancer. Remember, in a famine situation, you are locked in to eating what you have stored. Try to eliminate as many chemicals as you can.

If the product is *under* 75% protein, it may not be a good buy.

4. **Ingredient Ratio.** By law it is required that all ingredients be listed on the label in descending order. The first ingredient is a tip-off. If it is some form of soya protein, it probably has a low P.E.R. If it starts with casein, it has a chance of having a high P.E.R.

5. **Amino Acid Profile.** A good concentrate will list the amino acid profile in comparison to the ideal percentages published by the Food and Agriculture Organization of the United Nations. It should equal or exceed those ideal percentages.

6. **Extra Lysine and Tryptophan.** It should definitely *exceed* the ideal for lysine and tryptophan. Remember, we will be using this concentrate to replace the lysine and tryptophan in our dried milk, wheat, and T.V.P. where they are missing or unavailable.

7. **P.E.R.** If it doesn't make reference to P.E.R. on the label, it doesn't have a good one.

8. **Low Temperature Process.** The concentrate

should be made from low temperature dried ingredients, as high temperatures affect the P.E.R. All protein processors buy from a few raw material suppliers. Some buy "low-temp" ingredients, which are more expensive, some use "hi-temp" ingredients, which are cheaper; and the label information on the final product looks the same.

Mixing and blending processes should be at low temperatures (under 100°).

Again, if they don't brag about it on the label or in their literature, they probably have nothing to talk about.

9. **Digestive Enzymes.** Pure proteins can be hard to digest. A conscientious manufacturer will use a combination of digestive enzymes in the process. This accomplishes good blending without heat and partially predigests the protein for easy digestion and absorption. It compensates for some of the missing enzymes that have been destroyed by heat in the dry milk in which it will be mixed, so that all the amino acids will be available to the body. (See Chapter VIII for information about enzyme destruction and digestion). The best enzymes are papain (from papaya), bromelain (from pineapple) and pancreatin (an animal enzyme). It should have at least two of these, and preferably all three.

10. **Yeast.** This means a good B-complex profile if yeast is included. It should be "primary grown". Even if there is no B Vitamin information on the label, if yeast is among the first five ingredients listed, the B vitamins will probably be there in significant quantities.

11. **No Dry Skim Milk Powder.** If this is included in

the product, and is on the label near the beginning of the ingredient list, you know much of the product is affected by the factors listed in Chapter VIII on the Deadly Errors. Most of the lysine in the product will be from that source, and may be unavailable. This is true even if it is a "low-temperature" dried milk. If you want dry skim milk, you can get it a lot cheaper than at protein concentrate prices.

contain egg protein. This seems like a good idea, as eggs have the highest P.E.R. But it's not that simple.

The drying of eggs is a difficult process, and definitely damages the amino acids. Also, egg protein is difficult to work with because of the danger of salmonella infection. For that reason, most protein manufacturers won't use it. To avoid the salmonella problem, most processors use synthetic egg, which reduces the value, in my opinion. I don't like plastic food!

13. **Sweeteners Used.** In order to be palatable, sweeteners are often used. Remember, raw sugar, Kleen Raw Sugar, and Turbinado sugar are merely sucrose — table sugar — in a slightly less refined form, with all of its disadvantages. If the label lists glucose, dextrose, or corn syrup, this is a simple sugar which has the highest insulin requirement. This means if you are a diabetic or a hypoglycemic (low blood sugar) or are inclined to obesity, these are undesirable for your health.

Fructose (a natural fruit sugar) is, in my opinion, the most desirable sugar. It is twice as sweet as other sugars, so you only require half as much for good sweetening. It has a negligible insulin requirement, so it is safe for the diabetic, the hypoglycemic and the obese. It is more expensive than the other sugars, but worth it because of its special advantages. It also has a high "protein sparing action", meaning that it is used in the body for energy in such a way that you have no need to break down as much protein for energy. This "spares" the protein to do the things that *only* protein can do.

14. **Honestly Labeled.** There is a top selling brand, that is touted as a "97% protein powder". It is a perfect example of legal but deceptive labeling. The label looks something like this:

ONE OUNCE CONTAINS
Protein (dry basis) 97% . . . 17 grams.

At first glance this is 97% protein. But there is some data missing. There are 28.35 grams in an ounce. 17 grams is *not* 97% of one ounce (28.35 grams). It is only about 60%. What does the label mean then? It simply means that 17 grams out of every ounce (28.35 grams) is a protein powder made up of 97% protein and something else. (Probably fiber, moisture, etc.)

This may sound complicated, but go back and look it over. It's legal, but deceptive.

(As this book went to press, the manufacturer of this product signed a consent degree with the FTC, agreeing to change the label, without admitting any guilt.)

There are other small deceits used in labeling, such as: including in the product nutritional analysis the protein content of the milk in which it will be mixed, without making that fact clear, and *without* showing you an analysis *without* the milk, so you can see just how much protein is contributed by the milk, and how much is contributed by the product.

Other Protein Sources

You can get protein value from nuts, seeds, beans, grains, sprouted grains, canned tuna, canned meats, bouillion and dried eggs. Most of these foods are low P.E.R. Some are rich in fats and oils, so shelf life is limited, as they are subject to rancidity. Most are high in carbohydrates, so their intake may have to be limited. But they can all contribute some value, *especially if taken with your protein concentrate.*

How Much Do You Need?

Twenty-five to thirty pounds of a good concentrate will provide about 80% of your protein requirements for one year, when taken with reconstituted dry milk. The other protein sources in your diet can supply the rest of your requirements *especially when taken in the same meal with your concentrate.*

CHAPTER XV

The Bullseye — Vitamins and Minerals and E.F.A.

Vitamins represent problems in a food storage program.

1. *The vitamin and mineral values of storage foods are difficult to determine,* especially in commercial storage programs. *First,* this is due to erratic values in the *fresh* product, depending on degree of product maturity, length of storage *before* processing, soil (for mineral and protein values), and differing strains of fruit, vegetables and grain. *Second,* various processes, such as blanching, drying, canning, and even some chemical additives, reduce the vitamin and mineral content. The variance from standard tables can be two or threefold. *Third,* the prime processor of dried foods may have stored his dried product for awhile, uncanned and unprocessed for long term storage, perhaps for weeks or months before shipping it to the canner. This can result in substantial losses of undetermined magnitude.

2. Vitamin and mineral potency can diminish on your shelf to an unknown degree. Canned goods (wet

pack) are particularly vulnerable to vitamin deterioration — some experts say 50% to 80% within a year. Dehydrated fruits and vegetables lose value to a lesser degree, and the lowest shelf loss is found in nitrogen-pack dehydrated and freeze dried foods. Often when claims are made for shelf life, they just mean it won't rot, and there is no reference to nutritional values.

3. There are losses in cooking on the consumer end.

Nutrition and the F.D.A.

The Food and Drug Administration has long claimed you could get all the vitamins and minerals from a typical American diet of readily available foods. This claim, however, has been loudly disputed by such authorities as Dr. Roger Williams, (a member of the National Research Council of the National Academy of Sciences, which sets the Recommended Daily Allowances (R.D.A.) for various nutrients, and the discoverer of pantothenic acid, a member of the B complex), Dr. Szent-Gjorgi (Nobel Laureate and the first to synthesize Vitamin C), Dr. Linus Pauling (Biochemist and Nobel Laureate) and a host of other mainstream scientific luminaries. Even the Department of Agriculture has issued a massive report called, "An Evaluation of Research in the United States on Human Nutrition — Benefits From Nutrition Research", reporting serious malnutrition, cutting across economic lines, especially among children and the aged, which completely disputes the F.D.A. position.

Unfortunately, the F.D.A., like most government agencies, goes blindly on like a mindless robot juggernaut, freezing into law its unscientific and controversial position. The best that can be said for this view is that it is one side of an ongoing scientific dispute. This has led through natural evolution to a bias against vitamin and mineral supplements by the F.D.A. and a 12 year concerted effort to make supplements difficult to manufacture, obtain or afford.

Even if the basic premise were true, that Americans are well-nourished from the typical diet of processed, poorly selected, devitalized, over-chemicalized foods that occupy an increasing percentage of our intake, this premise founders on the realities of food storage — namely that **a wide variety of foods will not be available, the stress of famine increases nutritional requirements, and long term storage required compromises in food selection, processing, and preparation.**

The only logical answer is nutrient supplementation. In most storage programs, supplementation is an afterthought. This is due to lack of knowledge, and anti-supplement bias on the part of those who have great influence on food storage programs, and should know better.

A classic example of this occurred early in 1974 in the Relief Society Organization of the Church of Jesus Christ of Latter-day Saints. This wonderful organization (of which my wife is an enthusiastic member) is charged with the nutrition education of the Church, and has a series of nutrition lessons being taught Church-wide. Now, I don't agree with everything in those lessons, but they are unquestionably valuable and useful.

At the Annual Conference of the Relief Society,

however, a handout was distributed to those in attendance, prepared by a B.Y.U. Professor, which was a rehash of an old F.D.A. propaganda blast aimed at the Supplement industry, at the so-called "Quacks and Faddists".

Now, no one denies that there are "quacks" and "faddists". But this vicious document lumped those who merely agree with the current minority side of this ongoing dispute, with the crooks and charlatans, and tried to discredit them by association, an association which exists only in the imagination of the F.D.A.

For example, according to this document, *you* are quack if you believe:

1. Our soil has lost its vitamins and minerals (even a little bit)!

2. Modern processing removes vitamins and minerals from foods.

3. Vitamins from natural sources are better.

4. That vitamin supplements are good nutrition insurance.

The result of this blast, which was faithfully taught by thousands of dedicated Relief Society teachers, was tragic.

The women who are the nutritionists in each L.D.S. home, whose children so often start the day with "plastiflakes shot from guns, with its five essential preservatives", whose teen-agers think a Big Mac is a gourmet dinner, who might have been able to compensate partly for the media-influenced nutritional atrocities our children commit, did not do so. After all, didn't the "Church" say vitamin supplements were unnecessary?

Of course, "the Church" didn't say so. Some misguided zealots said so, and unfortunately it got into channels.

Also, thousands of fine women who buy and use supplements, or who, out of a sense of dedication or to make a little pin money, sell them to their friends as distributors of these products, found themselves labeled "quacks" and "faddists". My wife was heartbroken. My secretary, who was not L.D.S., but who was attending Relief Society was offended and alienated, to be painted as a "quack" or faddist. One serious effect of this incident has been to cause people to conclude that supplements would be of no value in a storage program.

The President of one of the leading companies in the supplement field called on me and asked me to assist in preparing a document responding to this error. We prepared a paper and a meeting was obtained with the Presidency of the Relief Society by this gentlemen, and the problem was laid out before them. They were shocked, as the propaganda had been distributed without their knowledge or approval. Shortly afterward, the following statement was graciously released by the Presidency:

> "In connection with the teaching of the family health lessons, some reports have come to the General Board of extreme positions being taken by some members in discussions relating to food supplements. The material in the lessons themselves is not in question, but in view of these extreme views, the general board wishes to state that the Church is not against

> food supplements, the Church is in favor of all forms of good nutrition. No blanket rule on nutrition applies to every individual inasmuch as body chemistries vary, and each individual would respond to his nutritional needs as suggested by the medical opinion he seeks.
>
> "The objective of the family health lessons that are being studied worldwide is to encourage the sisters to prepare good nutritious meals for themselves and their families. It is not the purpose of these lessons to have local sisters take sides on questionable matters, not to endeavor to settle questions on matters that are under study at the present time in the scientific field.
>
> "We would suggest to teachers once again that in presenting their lessons they adhere closely to material which is presented in the manual."

Unfortunately, it didn't receive the attention the original paper did, but it demonstrates that this fine organization is *not* anti good nutrition.

Food Storage "Quacks"?

Be sure this bias does not blind you to a critical fact.

The only way you can be sure of the nutritional value of your storage program is with supplements.

For your information, here is a partial text of our answer to the "Quackery" charge:

> "Recently, there has been an apparent

rash of propaganda blasts by the F.D.A. aimed at so-called "health quacks" and "faddists". These attacks have been channeled through schools, the media, the womens' Church Auxiliary organizations.

"*We have no objection to literature which takes a position contrary to that which we believe to be true in health matters.* We do intend, however, to vigorously fight any such literature which states such positions as indisputable, uncontroversial, scientific fact, as well as literature which attacks those who disagree with bureaucratic edicts, and label them as "quacks" and "faddists".

"You should be properly armed with appropriate answers to those attacks, so that you can answer them *calmly, carefully, and responsibly.*

"In order to effectively counter, you must first understand the strategies used. Be alert to the following tactics:

1. **"Guilt by Association" method**

They lump together all who disagree including the lunatic fringe and the qualified scientist and researcher and apply easy labels like "quack":, "faddist", "nut". Thus the responsible critic is discredited.

2. **"Straw Man" Technique**

They make an outrageous statement that no responsible nutrition advocate ever made, then thoroughly demolish it.

They make reasonable, sound statements, and state or imply that the "quacks" and "faddists" don't agree with them. (A variation of the "Straw Man" technique.)

3. **"Big Brother Knows All"**

Beware of the Bureacrats who preface statements with "There is no evidence . . .", or "I know of no evidence", etc. The implication being that the statement or position under discussion is false. Not so. What they are really saying is "I'm not up on the latest nutritional research" or they are deliberately attempting to discredit or cast doubt on an issue.

"Incredibly, this technique was used by Dr. Ogden C. Johnson, the FDA's Director of Nutrition when he ordered a Pantry Pride food store to remove signs showing amounts of saturated or unsaturated fats in foods. Despite the fact that this program was developed by local doctors for the guidance of their patients to help their arteries and hearts, Dr. Johnson was quoted in the "*Prince George's County Sentinel*" (November 15, 1972) as saying, "There is no shred of evidence to prove that diet reduces the threat of heart disease". Hardly a Cardiologist in America would agree with that statement!

"One standard piece of propaganda comes from the FDA and is entitled "Nutrition Nonsense — and Sense". It lists twelve alleged

"Claims" made by "Quacks" and the "Facts" about them. Because the attack is so broad, involving so many areas of the natural food and nutrition movement, it is not our objective here to defend them all, but we would like to tackle some of them.

"We have chosen four areas to defend. We have, in each instance, quoted directly from the FDA paper the statement we "quacks" are alleged to be making, and the FDA's attempt at refuting that claim. We have labeled these statements (with perhaps a little heavy handed irony) "Quack Claim", and "FDA Fact", (alleged). We have followed each such "Claim" and "Fact" with a partial refutation entitled "Our Position"!

Supposed "Quack Claim" #1

Our soil has lost its vitamins and minerals; our food crops have little nutritional value.

FDA "Fact" (Alleged)

"In the commercial production of food crops, fertilizers are applied in order to produce satisfactory yields. The nutrients which promote good plant growth are added to the soil in these fertilizers, and the food crops produced contain the expected nutritional value".

Our Position.

In 1965 in a memo written by Dr. Homer Hopkins of the Nutritional Research Branch of the Division of Nutrition, U.S. Dept. of Agriculture to the chief of his department, Dr. Hopkins states, "The statement that 'the nutritional value of our crops are not significantly affected by either the soil or kind of fertilizer used' cannot be defended". He cited 16 studies to make his point.

Dr. Wm. A. Albrecht, Professor Emeritus of Soils, U. of Missouri, attacked the FDA soil myth in the *Consumer Bulletin* of January 1961. The editors in their introduction to the article, wrote "Professor Albrecht shows that the health of animals is directly dependent upon the quality of soils that produce food and forage crops. It must follow that human beings are subject to similar effects".

Supposed "Quack Claim" #2

"Modern processing removes most of the vitamins and minerals in foods".

FDA "Fact" (Alleged)

"This is not true. While any type of processing, including simple cooking, tends to reduce to some extent the nutrient content or quality of foods, modern processing methods are designed to keep such losses as low as possible. In many instances, nutrients are restored by enrichment after processing".

Our Position.

The Congressional Record of November 15, 1971, quotes Dr. R. E. Hein, Manager of Food Research for the H.J. Heinz Co. (a major food processor!) "Most vitamins disintegrate in air, heat and light. When fresh vegetables containing these nutrients are cooked, the losses range up to 40% for Vitamin A, 100% for Vitamin C, 75% for Niacin, 80% for thiamine and 55% for Vitamin E".

As for "enrichment" being the answer, according to Dr. Walter Mertz, Chief of the U.S. Dept. of Agriculture's Vitamin and Mineral Nutrition Laboratory, milling wheat into white flour removes most of the trace element content, including zinc, manganese, copper, cobalt.

These are not replaced through "enrichment". Twenty six known nutrients are removed. Eight are restored in part. If I took $26.00 out of your purse and put back in $8.00 and claimed to have "enriched" you, would you believe me?

Supposed "Quack Claim" #3

"Synthetic vitamins are dead and ineffective; vitamins from natural sources are much better".

FDA "Fact" (Alleged)

"Vitamins are specific chemical compounds, and the human body can use them equally well whether they are synthesized by a chemist or by nature".

Our Position

First — no-one should say "Synthetic vitamins are dead and ineffective". We simply say they duplicate some, but not all of the functions of the natural.

British Researcher, Isobel W. Jennings of University College of the University of Cambridge, speaks of the comparison between synthetic and natural vitamins in her book, *"Vitamins in Endocrine Metabolism"*, (Charles C. Thomas, 1970).

"The close relations, although useful in many ways, pose some problems in that they may have only a fraction, whether large or small of the biolgical activity of the natural product". She points out that Vitamin C, for example, is chemically identical to the natural vitamin and an equally effective anti-oxident, yet does not have the same value in promoting the health of the capillaries.

Writing in the August 27, 1973, issue of the *Journal of the American Medical Association,* Dr. Samuel Ayers, Jr., an M.D. from Los Angeles, disputed the contention of Margarita Magy, M.S., of the AMA Department of Foods and Nutrition.

She had made the statement (J.A.M.A., July 2, 1973) that bio-chemically, a vitamin has a single molecular structure and it didn't make any difference if it was natural or synthetic because the body couldn't tell the difference.

"This may be true of some vitamins," Dr. Ayers wrote, "but it is definitely not true of Vitamin E (tocopherol), in which the alpha fraction contains virtually all of the therapeutically active principle. D-alpha-tocopheryl acetate is derived from natural sources, such as wheat germ oil, whereas dl alpha-tocopheryl acetate is the synthetic form.

"While they may appear identical chemically, they affect polarized light differently and in animal experiments the d or natural form is considerably more active than the dl or synthetic form", he wrote.

Dr. Ayers cited several sources to back up his statement including Roels who said: "The Animal Research Council subcommittee for Vitamin E standards has shown that the relative potency of d alpha-tocopheryl acetate is 1.2 times (20 percent) greater than the dl form (Nutrition Reviews, 24:33-37,1967). Another report which appeared in *Animal Science* (27:58,1968) indicated that the natural Vitamin E has approximately 36 percent greater activity than does the synthetic form.

"In order to obtain the maximum therapeutic effect from Vitamin E," Dr. Ayers concluded, "The physician should specify d-alpha-tocopheryl acetate."

Supposed "Quack Claim" #4

"Everyone should take vitamins, just to be sure".

FDA "Fact" (Alleged)

"Very few of us eat exactly the same foods as our neighbors eat. There is some variation that makes our diet different from everyone else's. It is variety that helps assure adequate nutrition for most of us. Most healthy individuals whose diet regularly includes even modest amounts of meat and eggs, milk products, fruits and vegetables, bread and other cereal products need not resort to dietary supplements. Some persons under a doctor's care or in institutions need dietary supplements because of special conditions which greatly restrict their ability to eat a well-balanced diet. Modest supplementation with certain vitamins is generally recommended during infancy, pregnancy and while breast feeding".

Our Position

We have researched the literature for verification of our position. For just one vitamin, Vitamin C, dozens of articles have appeared in respected, main stream medical, biochemical and nutrition journals, recommending routine supplementation ranging from 200 to 2,000 milligrams a day if you have any of the following conditions in your life: tobacco, alcohol, smog, stress, "the Pill", hormone or cortisone therapy, radiation therapy, frequent colds, excess sugar intake, not enough sleep, surgery, emotional problems. Have we missed anyone?

One citation should suffice. Drs. Andersen, Reid and Beaton report in the *Canadian*

Medical Association Journal (Sept. 23, 1972) their tests on a large number of students to determine the value of Vitamin C as a cold preventative. Their avowed purpose was to explode the Vitamin C "Myth". They reported that "our finding that disability was substantially less in the vitamin group (than in the control group) was entirely unexpected, and may have important theoretical and practical implications". They found that the daily use of large amounts of Vitamin C resulted in sharply reduced incidence of colds, and among those who did contract colds, fewer symptoms and 30% fewer days of disability.

Remember, that in conteracting these ridiculous charges, your objective is to let these usually misguided or misinformed people know that there is another side to the story, and that they have been duped into taking sides in a scientific dispute which is by no means resolved. They must know that the so-called "facts" are but one side of an on-going debate, and fairness requires that the other side be heard. Inform them that the U.S. Department of Agriculture has recently published a massive report on Human Nutrition directly disputing virtually everything said in these F.D.A. propaganda blasts.

In the final analysis, each concerned person must hear *both* sides of the issue, and decide for themselves."

Natural vs. Synthetic Vitamins

As you can see from the foregoing document, it is the "official" word that there is no difference between "synthetic" and "natural" vitamins. There is one essential difference, however, that relates to food storage.

When a vitamin is derived from a natural source, it is generally a concentrate of a food that is rich in that vitamin, with fat, moisture and fiber removed. An example, would be a B complex tablet or capsule derived from yeast. In the yeast are so called "impurities", food factors other than the vitamins and minerals on the label. This could include trace minerals, enzymes, amino acids, and controversial nutrients. There are also "unknowns" — undiscovered factors which are suspected but not identified.

For example, liver had an unknown energy factor that gave laboratory animals several times the endurance of the animals that were fed only the nutrients known to be in liver. This element has been identified, (but not synthesized) only recently.

In its attempts to standardize vitamins, the F.D.A. has proposed regulations requiring manufacturers of supplements to exclude *Choline and Inisotol* from supplements, calling them "of unproven value in human nutrition". Many nutritionists, M.D.'s and biochemists feel they are essential, and are part of the B-complex. This is an unresolved scientific dispute.

If the food crisis came before the dispute was resolved, would you rather have it *in* your storage program, or *excluded* from your program? If it's not essential, you have nothing to lose by having it. If it is essential, having it, or not having it is critical.

Your body doesn't wait for the government to make it official before it uses it.

Natural Vitamin Does It

A natural vitamin will usually have these controversial factors as "naturally occurring" factors, and the "unknowns" are there, even if they don't show on the label.

The synthetic vitamin will have *only* what is on the label — chemically pure vitamins, combined according to the chemists opinion of the body's needs, based on the latest government regulations. It generally takes from 5 to 20 years from the time of discovery of a nutrient, for it to be synthesized, Recommended Daily Allowances to be established, and for the government to recognize the need for it. In a food crunch, you can't take the chance of incompleteness.

How to Read Labels

There are hundreds of brands of vitamins available. There is also a lot of deceptive humbuggery in the field, particularly in labeling them "natural".

Vitamins are sold in three basic forms: **Synthetic, Crystalline, and Natural.**

Synthetic: Created in the laboratory from organic substances unrelated to the foods in which the vitamin would occur naturally, such as synthetic Vitamin C from glucose. Such synthetic vitamins can be legally called "Organic", so the word "organic" means nothing. Anything which contains a carbon molecule is organic, such as coal or petroleum.

Crystalline. This started as a natural vitamin source and has gone through a series of solvent baths until only the pure, isolated, single vitamin in crystalline form remains, such as B-1 or B-3. None of the so-called "impurities" are left. If they want to make a "B-Complex", they recombine and mix until they have the ratio the chemists and the F.D.A. say meet the **Recommended Daily Allowances.** Crystalline vitamins can legally be labeled *Natural.*

Natural. I define this as a natural vitamin source with only moisture, fat and fiber removed. A true natural Vitamin C could be a whole citrus concentrate, or a concentrate of Rose Hips or Acerola Cherries.

How to Tell the Difference

When you examine the claims of the various brands, bear in mind that it is legal to make it from all crystalline sources, with a substantial amount of synthetic, and still call it "Natural and Organic". The F.D.A. allows this, in my opinion, because it is their official position that there is no difference between synthetic and natural, so "what the heck".

The following table should help you:

Item	If source given is:	It is:
Vitamin A	Fish oils	Natural
	Acetate	Synthetic
	Palmitate	Synthetic
	Lemon Grass	Synthetic
Vitamin B1 (Thiamine)	Yeast	Natural
	Thiamine Mononitrate	Synthetic
	Thiamine Hydrochloride	Synthetic
Vitamin B2 (Riboflavin)	Yeast	Natural
Pantothenic Acid	Yeast, Rice Bran or Liver	Natural
	Cal Panto or Calcium Pantothenate	Synthetic
Vitamin B6 (Pyridoxine)	Yeast	Natural
	Pyridoxine Hydrochloride	Synthetic

Item	If source given is:	It is:
Vitamin B12	Liver	Natural
	Microorganism fermentation	Crystalline
	Cobalamin Concentrate	Crystalline
Paba (Para-aminobenzoic Acid)	Yeast	Natural
	Para-aminobenzoic Acid	Probably synthetic
Folic Acid	Yeast or Liver	Natural
	Pteroylglutamic Acid	Synthetic
Inisotol	Soybeans	Natural
	Reduced from Corn	Crystalline
Choline (Basic constituent of Lecithin, used as a Lipotropic Adjunct)	Soybeans	Natural
	Choline Chloride	Synthetic
	Choline Bitartrate	Synthetic

Biotin	Liver	Natural
	d-biotin	Synthetic
Nicotinic Acid (see Niacin)		
Niacin	Yeast	Natural
	Niacinamide	Crystalline
Vitamin C (Ascorbic Acid)	Citrus, Rose Hips, Acerola Berries	Natural
	Ascorbic Acid	Probably synthetic some may be co-natural
Vitamin D	Fish Oil	Natural
	Irradiated Ergosterol (yeast)	Crystalline
	Calciferol	Synthetic

Item	If source given is:	It is:
Vitamin E	Wheat Germ oil	Natural
	dl-alpha tocopherol	Synthetic
	d-alpha tocopheryl acetate	Crystalline
	d-alpha tocopherol succinate	Crystalline
Vitamin K	Alfalfa	Natural
	Menadione	Synthetic

MINERALS

Item	Source	Remarks
Calcium	Bone Meal	Very low potency. Bulky and little used. If used it is generally mixed with a much higher potency dicalcium or tri-calcium phosphate
	Dicalcium phosphate	Bone meal that has had the fat and protein burned out

	Calcium Lactate	
Phosphorus	Naturally-occurring with calcium (see calcium phosphate above)	From milk.
Iodine	Seaweed or Kelp	A natural organic source
	Potassium Iodide	A chemical combination
Iron	Ferrous Gluconate	Iron combined with organic acid derived from glucose
	Ferrous Sulphate	An inorganic chemical
Copper	Copper Gluconate	Copper combined with corn-starch
Magnesium	Magnesium phosphate	An inorganic chemical
	Magnesium Sulfate	Occurs in nature as the mineral Keiserite

Item	Source	Remarks
Potassium	Potassium Borate	An inorganic chemical
	Potassium Carbonate	Occurs in sedimentary earth deposits
Manganese	Manganese Glycerophosphate	An inorganic chemical
	Manganese Citrate	Manganese combined with an organic citric acid
Cobalt	Cobalt Sulphate	An inorganic chemical
Flourine	Edible bone phosphate	A natural organic source
	When source not given, usually	An inorganic chemical
Nickel	Nickel Sulphate	An inorganic chemical
Zinc	Zinc Sulphate	An inorganic chemical
	Zinc Acetate	An inorganic chemical

Bibliography:

"Vitamins in Medicine — Bicknell and Prescott

"Chemistry and Physiology of Vitamins" — H. R. Rosenberg, Sc. D.

"New and Non-Official Remedies" 1952 Edition, issued under the direction and supervision of the Council on Pharmacy and Chemistry of the American Medical Association.

"Merck Index"

Why Do Natural Vitamins Cost More?

1. **Harder to make.** The manufacturer is working with biologically active substances containing enzymes, etc. It is difficult to maintain uniformity, as his raw materials vary in color, potency, and taste, as all natural foods tend to do. It can be done, but it is more costly. The synthetic manufacturer is dealing with inert substances. Synthetics are cheap to make, and easy to handle because of their low biological activity.

2. **Smaller Volume.** There just isn't as large a quantity of natural vitamins made and sold.

3. **Smaller Outlets.** They are generally sold through health food stores or direct neighborhood distributors. Their small volume requires a larger mark-up to be profitable enough to provide incentive.

Is It Worth It?

For a survival program, definitely. We've already covered several reasons earlier. We don't need to debate the chemical differences in the natural molecule. Just remember "Completeness" as the key word. You don't want to get caught with the unknown factors missing, just because they haven't been identified yet.

Remember, your stored foods, no matter how carefully you select, simply don't have "standard" nutritional values. Supplementation removes the uncertainty.

Which Natural Vitamins to Store

1. **Examine the label.** Choose only "all-natural". You will undoubtedly be surprised to see how hard they are to find. If the ingredient sources are *not* given, it's synthetic.

2. **Soft Gelatin Capsule.** This extends shelf life, especially if there are oil concentrates. Hard capsules develop hairline cracks and admit air which hastens oxidation. The soft capsule protects the essential fatty acids, if they are there in the first place.

3. **Prepared For Long Term Storage.** Your *daily* supply should be in separate sealed plastic packs, and the product should be canned.

Special Problems

Any multi-vitamin supplement will fall short of meeting your storage requirements in two ways.

Vitamin C

This vitamin, especially if it is all natural, and contains the Bioflavenoids, is bulky. There is probably enough C in the multi-supplement to prevent scurvy, but not enough to meet the requirements of stress. Most experts agree that stress destroys vitamin C in the body. Under stress, hormone output increases, especially the Adrenal hormones. One of the concentration points of vitamin C is the Adrenal Cortex. This disappears rapidly under stress.

Vitamin C is an integral part of your white blood cells, and as they multipy when you are fighting infection, you use up Vitamin C rapidly.

Connective tissue (collagen) requires vitamin C, and your body can't make collagen without vitamin C. When you are healing from surgery, or an injury, collagen is the repair tissue, so vitamin C is used up rapidly.

As vitamin C is bulky, and you need a lot under stress, store some in addition to your multivitamin capsules. You can also increase your vitamin C content by sprouting grains and seeds. This helps some, but not enough. The experts differ, but in my opinion at least 200 milligrams per day per person is advisable, and more would be better. Be sure it is in dark brown bottles or in cans, and is sealed air-tight until you begin to use that particular bottle or can. After it has been opened, it has a shelf life of about one year, if reasonably protected. Air and light are vitamin C enemies.

Processing of storage foods damages the vitamin C content more than any other vitamin. You can't afford to get sick if we have a breakdown of services in this country. You may not be able to get to the doctor quickly, and he may not have a supply of "wonder drugs". Vitamin C is believed by many authorities to be nature's most potent protective factor. Man, the guinea pig, the apes, and a species of Indian fruit bat, are the only animals that don't manufacture their own vitamin C in the liver. If we took as much vitamin C for our body weight, as other animals manufacture for their body weight, *we would take between 5,000 and 20,000 milligrams a day!* So much for the R.D.A. of 60 milligrams!

Calcium

The kind of storage program we recommend will create a calcium deficiency, unless you supplement with additional calcium. Your multivitamin will not contain enough, because calcium is too bulky and would be incompatible with the oils.

Wheat and other grains contain large amounts of phosphorous. You need two parts of calcium to one part of phosphorous in your diet. Too much phosphorous creates an imbalance resulting in a calcium deficiency. Wheat also contains phytic acid, which prevents the absorption and utilization of calcium.

Calcium isn't just for bones and teeth. A deficiency can cause insomnia, headaches, irritability, muscle cramps, irregular heartbeat, poor utilization of vitamins C and A, and a host of other problems. Small children, nursing mothers, adolescents, and the aged are particularly vulnerable. Your dry milk will provide some calcium, but not enough to meet your increased requirements.

A calcium supplement for storage should be low phosphorous (about 5% to 10% — as there is already plenty of phosphorous in your diet), from highly soluble sources (calcium gluconate and calcium lactate are best), and contain Vitamin D (natural, of course). It should also contain a hydrochloric acid source, such as Betain Hydrochloride, (from beet root) or glutamic acid.

Too Technical?

If you have plowed through this so far, you now know more about vitamins in storage than most people. If you have had trouble understanding it all, let me sum it up simply.

1. The vitamin and mineral content of most storage programs, even the the real good ones, is unknown.
2. Losses occur during storage — less for Nitrogen Pack than any other method.
3. Vitamin and mineral supplementation is the only positive way to ensure good nutrition in storage.
4. In my opinion, the natural variety is better, because it is more complete and gives more biological value for a given number of units or milligrams.
5. Vitamin C is a special protective factor needed in large quantities under stress. We are talking about famine as a stress situation.
6. Dangerous calcium deficiencies can develop due to high grain consumption.

Sprouting Seeds

When seeds and grains are placed in a sprouter, or even a damp paper towel, they sprout. The sprouts add color, roughage, and garnish to an otherwise dull diet. They can be used in salads, sandwiches, soups, etc.

Sprouting increases the vitamin content of the grain — as much as 600% for A and C. It helps, but don't over estimate its value. Seeds are low in these vitamins, so even a 600% increase isn't a lot, but remember, every little bit helps. Sprouts are so useful, and such a delightful addition, we have it next to the bullseye. You need to store about 15 to 20 lbs. per year per person.

Essential Fatty Acids

This represents the most neglected part of a storage program.

The Essential Fatty Acids (E.F.A., also known as "Vitamin F") are the "Assimilation Factors". Their function is to make it possible for the cell to receive nutrients and discharge wastes.

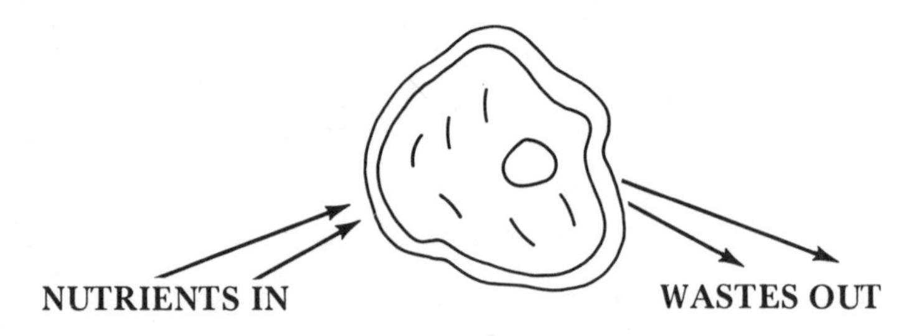

The cell wall or membrane has the ability to select from the bloodstream the nutrients it needs to function. If the cell wall is adequately supplied with E.F.A, it can do its job efficiently. Without E.F.A. it becomes leathery and impermeable, and the cell is poorly nourished. Toxins accumulate, it ages faster, and is subject to disease. E.F.A. makes nutrition possible. Without it, nutrients will be wasted, as assimilation becomes difficult or impossible.

You can get some E.F.A. from stored oils, but rancidity damages E.F.A. There is some in the wheat germ oil in your stored wheat, but E.F.A. is damaged in cooking or baking. E.F.A. is also altered *and* damaged in hydrogenation.

You should be sure that your supplements have E.F.A. in concentrated form in generous amounts. The soft gelatin capsule will protect it from rancidity.

Look on the label for Linoleic Acid, Linolenic Acid, and Arachidonic Acid. Look on the label or promotional literature for the "Essential Lipids and Sterols".

Sterols are made from E.F.A. in the body. They are components of hormones. You cannot make hormones without them. Under stress your body steps up its production of hormones, and sterols are used up. Your requirements will increase just when the available supply is disappearing. If you have a good supplement, containing enough, you don't have to worry.

CHAPTER XVI

The Bullseye Continued

"How Firm a Foundation, Ye Saints of the Lord"
(From an old American Hymn)

In the past few chapters we have shown you how to lay a sound foundation for your program. I hope you won't get tired of hearing this, but **once the basic needs for protein, vitamins, and minerals have been met, you have more freedom and flexibility in preparing the rest of your program.** Nutrition from here on is not so critical. You can select foods based on taste preference, being sure to meet your needs for adequate calories and bulk. This does not mean, however, that you should add junk foods.

Negative-Nutrition

Many common foods are actually anti-nutrition. For example, refined sugar has no food value other than refined carbohydrates, but it requires substantial amounts of the B-complex to be metabolized. So it robs your tissues, or other foods in your digestive tract to get those vitamins. That means that it actually dilutes the value of other foods and increases the requirement for the B vitamins. Honey is sweeter, and does the same sweetening job with less carbohydrate, so we use it instead. White sugar has no place in our storage program. When you are totally dependent on what you have stored, you have to get maximum value from that storage. Don't undermine your program with negative-nutrients.

Advantages of the Bullseye Program

About this time, someone usually says, "Isn't it a good idea to get your nutrients from food instead of pills and concentrates?"

If you say that at this point, you either haven't read Part II of this book, or you haven't paid attention.

During normal times, you should strive for maximum nutrition from your food, and "supplements" are just that — "supplements" — fillers in the nutritional cracks, caused by poor food selection, ignorance, illness, or excessive reliance on convenience foods.

During the period when you would need your food supplies for survival, we aren't just filling in nutritional cracks. Let me list a few of the reasons, some of them already expressed previously, why supplements and concentrates should be the heart of your program, not just an afterthought.

Realism and Food Storage

It is unrealistic to think that if we have a famine that requires us to live off our stored reserves, that food will be our only problem. We could face a complete breakdown of law and order, transportation, and the restraints of civilization. There has never been an orderly, well-organized famine. If our economy or currency collapses, there will be no way to pay policeman, firemen and truck drivers. Food will not disappear entirely, but it could be dangerous to go out looking for it.

1. Supplements and concentrates are light-weight and compact. They are easily transported and easily concealed. A one-year supply of "bullseye" items for one person is only 35 lbs. and occupies a space only 2 feet by 2½feet by 1½feet high.

2. It is foolish to plan a program that assumes we will be living comfortably and securely, and will be able to cook and bake and prepare the foods in the way we are accustomed to. This will be true only to a limited extent.

3. The demands of storage for the long term require the omission of a lot of good foods we now eat, because they don't store well. Meat, fish, fowl, nuts, seeds, fats and oils are all impractical for anything other than short term storage. Fats and oils oxidize and go rancid, and rancid fats are not only unpleasant, they are dangerous, creating peroxides and "free radicals" which attack our cells and shorten life. Supplements can supply the nutrients these foods would have provided, *so balanced nutrition can be achieved without a balanced diet.*

Remember — diet is what goes into the mouth. Nutrition is what gets to the cells.

4. We could be faced with leaving our homes to escape urban chaos. I would have trouble hauling all ten of us, *and* 3,000 pounds of wheat *and* dozens of cases of dried foods. I *could* find room for my Bullseye program,

and my book on edible weeds and roots. I wouldn't like my diet, but I could survive, and I could perform physically, and I could enjoy good health for an extended period of time.

Face Facts

I believe we must recognize realities. If you store at all, prepare for all the conditions associated with famine. If and when this happens, the very fabric of society could be ripped to shreds. Life as we know it will not exist. I'll say it again, we will be eating for survival, not for receation. Stick with the basics.

The principle of supplementary nutrition in storage could be summed up by showing you a complete target. Note the arrows from each of the bullseye elements, connecting them to the foods they enhance, fortify and complete:

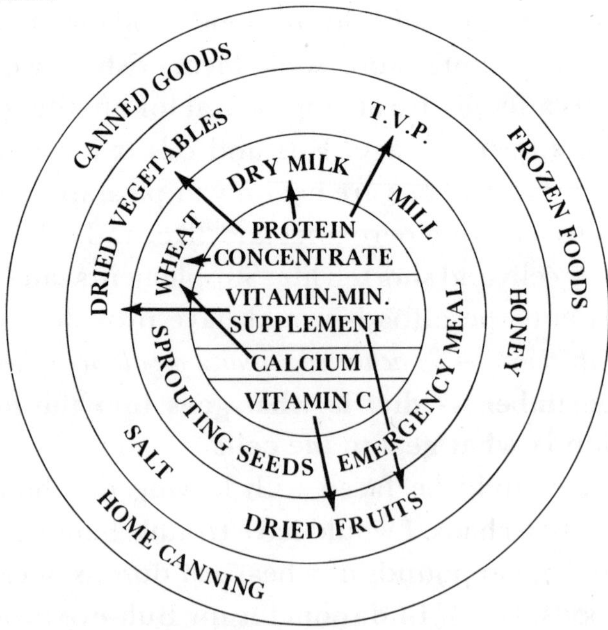

Without the Bullseye, your T.V.P., dry milk, wheat, and dried vegetables are incomplete proteins. Your vegetables and fruits are low in vitamins, You are deficient in calcium. You get poor assimilation in the cells due to a deficiency of E.F.A. With the Bullseye, you can be sure of super-fine nourishment.

CHAPTER XVII

Epilogue
The Loose Ends

As I make the final preparations for publication of this book, I'd like to let you in on one of the problems I've had to cope with while writing.

The news media have been full of articles showing the rapid development of the trends I've discussed. It is hard to make forecasts that stay ahead of reality. I've tried to update to the very last minute, but in the 60 days or so between now and actual publication, and in the additional weeks before you read this, events may have further borne out my forecasts.

Just before I decided to finalize the first edition, *The National Observer* printed a feature article entitled "The Spectre At the Feast". It was an alarming article which made statements which go far beyond what I've said about starvation and famine. It also names 1974 as the year to watch out for. Perhaps I'm too cautious, but I wouldn't have dared to be that specific.

> "While food shortages, hunger and starvation are still known and even tolerated in our times, the world's food prospects for 1974 are a serious unanswered question. If a coincidence of *not unlikely events occurs, 1974 holds the potential for a crisis in human suffering on a scale that may be unprecedented. And even if we are lucky and 1974 is ultimately recorded as a relatively "normal" food year, the potential for disaster will have been merely postponed. We will face the danger again in 1975, 1976, or 1977.*
>
> *"The danger can be reduced only by decisive action, and farsighted planning world-wide.*
>
> . . . "This is an ominous food year for three basic reasons. First, world food reserves are extremely low. Grain reserves, for example, have dropped to less than a month's supply from the 66-day supply of 1972, according to Lester Brown of the Overseas Development Council. Second, fertilizer is scarce because of the energy crisis. Third, there is growing evidence that the relatively stable and favorable climate of the past few decades is ending."

The author elaborates on the issue that, in my opinion, is the most dangerous threat of all — the vulnerability of the "green revolution" grains.

> . . . "The high-yield "miracle" crops used extensively in tropical and subtropical regions are very sensitive to soil fertilization (and

to optimum rainfall). It is therefore doubtful that countries such as India, dependent on imports of fertilizer and on stable water supply, can expect to achieve self-sufficiency in food production this year — even if the weather cooperates fully.

"That leads to another aspect of the 1970's food-production problem: *A benevolent climate can no longer be taken for granted.* Climate cannot be regarded as essentially constant, as we have commonly regarded it recently."

Regarding the world's ability to continuously expand the food supply to meet the needs of an ever-growing population, the article observes:

. . . "It is important to note that the total world food production fell 1 per cent in 1972, the first reduction since World War II.

" 'There is a very important climatic change going on right now,' says Reid Bryson of the University of Wisconsin, the most outspoken of the climatologists who have examined the evidence of climatic change. 'And it's not merely something of academic interest. *It is something that, if it continues, will affect the whole human occupation of the earth – like half a billion people starving.*' "

This is a human disaster on a scale undreamed of. This represents more deaths than the Black Plague, tuberculosis, cancer, heart disease, and all the wars since 1700 — combined!

The rest of the article sums up the problem and succinctly lays out some possible solutions. I believe it is a fitting summary for this book:

> . . . "Simply stated, the world has experienced an unusually benign and stable climatic span during the middle of the Twentieth Century. Simultaneous technological achievements in medicine and other fields permitted a vast increase in world population — and thus enormously increased demands for food.
>
> . . . "Thomas Malthus, Paul Ehrlich, and Lester Brown, among others, have warned us before. But in 1974 the "population bomb" may be ready to explode.
>
> "This seriousness of the food issue has largely eluded the public, in part because its complexities have been mired in scientific and technological controversy. We may also have become so weary of prophecies of doom and gloom that we figure that somehow we'll survive this crisis, too, if it comes.
>
> . . . "How much food-reserves insurance do we need? Can we afford to stockpile supplies if this means lost foreign exchange from international trade or increased prices at home from a reduced supply in the marketplace? How much are we willing to pay for world food security? In the short run, will the

public encourage decision makers to take the political risks associated with possible economic consequences of stockpiling reserves or, more drastically, reduced per-capita consumption? In a longer view, will the world move to limit population growth? Will nature?

"The odds for increased climatic variability are disturbing. To my mind the real question is, "Can we afford *not* to be prepared?"

. . . "If 1974 turns out to be a "bad" climatic year, there may be little we can do now to avoid the first thrusts of a world food crisis this year. There already are serious indications of drought-induced shortfalls in the wheat harvests in the United States, Canada, and the Soviet Union. But if we are lucky again — if this summer's weather is good and this year's harvest adequate — will we have the foresight to prepare for bad luck in future years?

. . . "Will North Americans curtail their food-consumption habits to save lives in India? Similar questions are likely to recur throughout the 1970's.

"This is not a new story; only the numbers have changed. Now we talk of billions of people. In Biblical times the numbers were in thousands. In Genesis 41 Joseph said to Pharaoh:

'Behold, there come seven years of great plenty in the land of Egypt. And then there

> shall arise after them seven years of famine; and all the plenty shall be forgotten in the land of Egypt. . . .
>
> 'Now therefore let Pharaoh look out to a man discreet and wise, and set him over the land of Egypt. Let Pharaoh do this and let him appoint overseers over the land, and take up the fifth part of the land of Egypt in the seven years of plenty. . . .
>
> 'And when all the land of Egypt was famished, the people cried to Pharaoh for bread . . . and Joseph opened all the storehouses, and sold unto the Egyptians; and the famine was sore in the land of Egypt. And all countries came into Egypt to Joseph to buy corn; because the famine was sore in all the earth'.
>
> "Maintaining food security is a plan as old as recorded history. Perhaps, in our age of space travel and mass media, we should relabel this ancient policy "The Genesis Strategy". Maybe then it might be pursued with new zeal. The lessons of history have been taught. Will we ever learn them?"

While discussing the solutions, I've tried to say the things that no one else has said. By the same token, I haven't tried to say the things that you could get from other books, such as storage methods, gardening, how to sprout grains and seeds, recipes, home drying and canning, etc.

For this information, I recommend the fine book "Making the Best of Basics". As of this date it costs $3.95. If you can't find it in a book store near you, write to me at P.O. Box 5381, Walnut Creek, Ca., 94596, and we'll tell you where you can get it. In fact, if you have any questions or comments, I or my staff will try to answer, if we aren't too swamped.

In the meantime, spread the word, warn your neighbor, and be a good example of systematic, careful, unafraid readiness. And remember, "Better a year too soon, than a day too late"! The 1974 drought is now history. Our troubles have begun. Or perhaps I should say, *your* troubles have begun. I'm ready.

Index